Thank you for purchasing my book. Never forget the names, faces of your employees family members for they are the unseen faces of safety.

"Safety, you can't afford not to have it."

*After reading my book please leve a review on Amazon and my websites **davidaward.com** and **davidawardsr.com***

THE FACES OF SAFETY

THE FACES OF SAFETY

*And Those Left Behind
When Tragedy Strikes*

DAVID A. WARD, SR.

Send comments and speaking and training requests to David A. Ward Sr., at
dward@sbdcs.com or www.davidawardsr.com
ISBN-13: 978-1-952163-17-3 (e-book)
ISBN-13: 978-1-952163-18-0 (paperback)
First edition published 2022.
Published by Redbaby Publishing, Inc., Clinton, MD 20735.
redbabypublishing@gmail.com

First Printing, 2023

To my family and friends who supported me in my USAF military career, Federal Bureau of Prisons, OSHA, Safety By Design Consulting Services, and Sentry Insurance. Thank you for making me who I am today. A special thank you to Amanda Kerr and Lisa Harwell who made publishing this book possible.

Table of Contents

Foreward

    This book speaks to the age-old question, "Have we done enough, or is there more we should be doing?" As a retired Safety Professional of over 40 years, I believe David A. Ward Sr. has undoubtedly shown us that we could never do enough regarding workplace safety as it evolves daily.

    Inside this book, you'll find a lifetime of experience, hard facts, and the compassion experienced by an extraordinary occupational safety and health professional. Dave and I have been professional colleagues for the past eleven years, and I understand his sincerity and deep passion for the safety and health profession. He asks tough questions of anyone who wants to lead an organization, no matter the company size. It's a compelling testimony about the importance of human life and those left behind whose struggles we'll never know. It's about the telling loss that shakes us when we don't keep our commitments or hold ourselves accountable for the safety of others.

    There's an abundance of valuable information combined with research, statistics, and resources that leaders can rely on to educate, inspire, connect, build policy upon, and compel their management teams to work towards to prevent workplace accidents. Every leader's goal should be to reduce or eliminate losses and create a high-performing and profitable company, business, and organization.

    I'll leave you with these thoughts if you truly value the lives of your employees, love leadership, and care about others as much as you care about becoming successful: you cannot go wrong using this book as your compass, your guidepost, or your workplace bible. Sharing this book with members of management, supervisors, and employees will demonstrate your investment in their lives and the lives of their families. It will be challenging, and the road will be paved with troubles and tough times, but you will persevere, knowing you have done the right thing. We can lead organizations to greatness, but not without investing in employees, supervisors, and managers who are compelled and committed to safety.

Managing and living this way will make you an impressive leader, which speaks volumes about how genuine you are in your commitment to safety which will make a tremendous impact on your business and future endeavors. As the author so passionately stated, "You can't put a price tag on that." Now that's a life worth living!

Randy Powell
Virtual/Keynote Speaker & Envision Success Coach
Creator of The Extraordinary Performance Success System &
Envision Success Coaching
909-720-0207

Praise for Dave Ward

As a world-renowned international motivational speaker, I have enjoyed working with David A. Ward Sr. for the past nine years as a friend and safety professional. He has tremendous credibility, work ethic, and a well-diversified background in the occupational safety and health field for the past 40 years, as evidenced in this book, *The Faces of Safety and Those Left Behind When Tragedy Strikes.*

Every chapter captures his passion, enthusiasm, and dedication to employee safety. I give my highest endorsement to *The Faces of Safety* because there is no other book that captures the thought-provoking, conversational, and heartfelt understanding of what families face when tragedy strikes involving loved ones who are injured or killed at work. This inspiring and captivating book will make you think about those left behind to carry on with life.

Lee Shelby

Amazon Bestselling Author of *No Hands and No Excuses: Living A No Excuses Life...No Matter What Happens to You!*

International Safety and Motivational Speaker

Lee Shelby Enterprise 12 Beckford Cove

Jackson, TN 38305 lee@leeshebly.com

Preface

In July 2011, I launched Safety By Design Consulting Services to provide affordable safety options for small-to-medium-sized companies. My desire was to have a positive impact in our communities, especially to companies that are forgoing investing in safety programs, procedures, and training because they believe they don't have the budget, manpower, or time to implement them.

I cannot overstate the importance of having a positive effect especially on the immigrant workforce, as they are the men and women being injured and killed doing jobs most of us wouldn't do for any amount of pay.

From 2017 to the present, I have worked as a Senior Safety Consultant, for Sentry Insurance, covering Indiana, Illinois, Michigan, Ohio, and parts of Tennessee and New York. I have analyzed loss information, created service plans, recommended safety and ergonomic improvements, and conducted mock OSHA inspections and OSHA 10–30-hour training sessions.

My goal in taking this job was to enhance my expertise in safety by managing a wide variety of safety programs for various manufacturing, retail, textile, mechanical, warehousing, distribution centers, utilities, furniture, power press, trucking, paper mills, packaging, and healthcare facilities. Another goal was to pay for my youngest daughter's college so that she would not be buried under student loan debt after graduation.

Based on the length and breadth of my experience, I began authoring this book, *The Faces of Safety*. This book is intended for CEOs, CFOs, middle managers, supervisors, employees, and anyone in business who cares about the real bottom line ... safety in the workplace. May we never forget "The Faces of Safety."

I have observed that safety policies at large companies are rooted in the notion that they're insured as a business and therefore, the insurance company will cover the losses for employees who are injured, maimed, or killed at work. This idea places a company price tag on an employee's life and is attributed to "the cost of doing business."

Small businesses and medium-sized companies that don't invest in safety for their employees rely on the notion that the cost of safety isn't something they can or want to pay for. In all actuality, employers need to invest in safety, as their employees are their most important asset. Where would companies be without employees?

Additionally, one of my goals is to utilize my education, experience, and expertise in safety to have a positive effect through persuasion, negotiation, conflict management, and resolution while selling the importance of investing in safety. If I can reach one person, save one life, stop one potential injury, have one CEO think differently about their employees and their safety, their family, and the financial impact on their company, I've been successful.

Those who are in business and strive to be CEOs, CFOs, executives, or supervisors and want to make a positive impact must always remember their employees and invest in their safety. You cannot place a price tag on the value of a life.

I want to speak for those who cannot speak, stand for those who cannot stand, and make the faces of safety a reason we invest in our workforce. We cannot forget about the faces and lives left behind: the wives, husbands, sons, daughters, and parents ... these are the faces of safety no one really thinks about, and they deserve better, wouldn't you agree? I have delt with family members who have been tragically injured and to be very honest, never thought about the affect it may have on those left behind. And for that, I apologize.

Introduction

On any given day, about a thousand people are severely injured, maimed, or killed at work. Could those accidents have been avoided or prevented? Important questions to ask include: Who is to care for them? How are their lives going to be affected? For those who didn't survive, who is left behind to pick up the pieces? Does anyone truly care?

Ask yourself one simple question: Would I allow a family member to work in these conditions? If the answer is no, you must then ask yourself why you're putting your employees in that position.

Value the lives of your employees. Don't gamble with them: they're priceless.

CHAPTER 1

Safety: An Investment or a Cost?

Carefulness costs you nothing. Carelessness may cost you your life.

"A small investment in your employees' safety, goes a long way in protecting your future and theirs."

Is safety an investment or a cost? That depends on your point of view, but the cost is significant either way you look at it. Safety for some companies is an expenditure they believe they cannot afford. For other companies, safety is a necessary evil; they must have it to stay in business. The cost is tremendous either way you look at it. The investment in establishing a safety program could be substantial on the one hand or minuscule on the other. But like anything else in business and in life, what you put into it is what you'll get out of it.

Safety programs are complex. The area is so broad and encompassing that you'll need a safety professional to provide you with the technical expertise and guidance to protect your employees and your company as well as the community.

For instance, what do you know about Occupational Safety and Health Administration (OSHA), the National Electric Code (NEC), the National Fire Protection Agency (NFPA), the Environmental

Protection Agency (EPA), or the state and federal Department of Transportation (DOT)? These are just a few agencies that could have an impact on your business.

OSHA ensures a safe and healthful working conditions for workers by setting and enforcing standards and by providing training, outreach, education, and assistance.

NFPA is a global self-funded non-profit organization, established in 1896 devoted to eliminating death, injury, property, and economic loss due to fire, electrical, and related hazards. They deliver information and knowledge through more than 300 consensus codes and standards research, training, education outreach, and advocacy. Consensus standards are recommendations or operating practices that are created by a group of experts that do not, by themselves have the ability to be enforced unless adopted by a regulatory body. As an example, the Occupational Health and Safety Act of 1970 provides guidance, reflect current expertise, and establish effective industry practices for a focused topic.

NEC is the benchmark for safe electrical design, installation, and inspection to protect people and property from electrical hazards. The NFPA publishes the NEC. This code changes every three years.

EPA ensures that Americans have clean air, land, and water. Reducing environmental risks.

DOT establishes drug and alcohol testing regulations to ensure that aircraft, trains, trucks, and buses are operated in a safe responsible manner. Under the DOT, several agencies are managed: Federal Aviation, Federal Motor Carrier Safety Admin, Federal Railroad, Federal Transit Admin, Pipeline & Hazardous Materials Safety Administration, etc.

Occupational Safety and Health Administration (OSHA)

Throughout my career I have had several encounters with each one of these organizations. As the Occupational Safety and Environmental Health Manager for the Federal Bureau of Prisons, OSHA visited several of my locations regarding inmate/staff complaints about safety issues from machine guarding of boring machines, drill presses, and trenching requirements to include proper use of the trench box otherwise called a "coffin box." These are usually steel or aluminum structures that are specifically designed to be used in trenches to avoid potential cave-ins and to protect utility workers while performing duties within a trench.

The most important thing to remember when utilizing a trench box is to make sure it is properly seated so cave-ins won't bury the feet of a worker in that area. If this were to occur it is tremendously difficult to get the dirt removed in a timely manner to reduce the potential of cutting off circulation at the feet. Remember, there is not a lot of space or time so rescue efforts could be hampered. Training on how to properly place the trench box is extremely important. You can also utilize either of the four systems of protection: benching, sloping, shoring, or shielding.

In my earlier days as the Occupational Safety and Environmental Health Manager for the Bureau of Prisons, CEO of Safety By Design Consultant Services, and even today as the Senior Safety Consultant guarding drill presses, safety is still an issue. The operator using the drill press or boring machine is expose to the rotating bit which has the potential of snapping as it meets the material and either striking or penetrating the body, face, or eyes. It's hard to believe that a guard that cost anywhere between $30-100 is not purchased and installed. This exposes the employee to a significant injury the company to an OSHA citation, and a mark on the company's reputation regarding employee safety.

I've been involved with EPA inspections relating to a boiler explosion, waste treatment plant overflow onto property grounds, and underground storage tanks that were leaching fuel into the soil. This encounter was very costly to the agency in time, productivity, and potential environmental exposure resulting in fines.

The boiler explosion had severe health consequences as the old boilers were wrapped in asbestos. When the explosion occurred, the asbestos became friable which simply means crumble and become airborne, releasing inhalable asbestos fibers. The explosion rocked the small powerhouse operations and caused a fire as well. We had to encapsulate the entire area, until we had it professionally evaluated and the asbestos removed as required by law.

Then, we had a treatment plant overflow causing an environmental issue at another facility. The overflow caused low levels of hydrogen sulfide, leading to respiratory irritation, nausea, and headaches. The overflow area had to be evaluated, and treated, and soil remediated. Then, it was inspected by the local EPA.

Afterward, we contracted the removal of several underground storage tanks due to the possibility of them leaching material into the ground. This was a lengthy process which required safety oversight, soil testing, and containment of the tanks. During this process we had to dig up the dirt around 18 inches below the lowest part of the tank and place the soil on a tarp so it could be aerated until the soil samples were at an acceptable level. Again, we had to work closely with the local OSHA/EPA offices.

Case Study: OSHA found violations related to machine guarding

Federal investigation finds Barberton toolmaker failed to properly protect drill press operators; three workers suffered preventable injuries.

Wright Tool Company faces proposed penalties of $152K

BARBERTON, OH. Since 1927, Wright Tool Company has forged wrenches, ratchets, sockets, and attachments with distribution to the automotive, hardware and industrial markets. In less than two years, three workers at a leading tool manufacturer in Barberton suffered injuries from unguarded machinery.

The latest injury occurred on Oct. 26, 2022, when a worker suffered a left thumb amputation while hand-feeding parts into a drill press using air-activated clamps. The worker had been on the job for just three months. In December 2020 and June 2022, two other workers performing similar tasks suffered laceration injuries.

Responding to the employer report of the amputation, investigators with the U.S. Department of Labor's Occupational Safety and Health Administration cited Wright Tool for one, willful violation of machine guarding standards, and two, serious and one other-than-serious violations. The company faces proposed penalties of $164,742.

"Wright Tool was aware of the need to improve their guarding but failed to do so," explained OSHA Area Director Howard Eberts in Cleveland. "Without proper guards and safety procedures in place, moving machine parts can cause severe workplace injuries. Employers have a legal responsibility to protect workers from hazards and train them on how to do the job safely."

OSHA found the company also failed to conduct hazard assessments to identify personal protective equipment needs and other requirements, did not test energy control procedures at least annually or train each employee to ensure they understood hazardous energy control procedures, and failed to enclose shafting.

Companies have 15 business days from receipt of the citations and penalties to comply, request an informal conference with OSHA's area director, or contest the findings before the independent Occupational Safety and Health Review Commission.

The Department of Transportation

My past also included crossing paths with the DOT regarding the Federal Motor Carrier safety Administration or the Surface Transportation Assistance Act (STAA) which address concerns regarding the infrastructure (highways and bridges). As a Federal Investigator for OSHA, I had to investigate incidents of retaliation for safety violations committed by the employer. Complaints ranged from employers failing to have pre and post vehicle inspections completed by the drivers, management of hours not properly documented, and drivers circumventing weigh stations due to the loads being overweight at the request of employers. As drivers voiced their safety concerns, employers then disciplined drivers by either firing the driver, reducing their hours, changing shifts, or placing disciplinary actions noted in the drivers' file. This investigation included taking statements from all parties, then writing a concise report identifying the possible violations. These violations could cost the company thousands to hundreds of thousands of dollars and a lot of time and legal fees.

The cost of safety and the lives lost shouldn't be considered just business.... it's more than that

As a federal investigator, I found it very easy to substantiate the employees' complaints which resulted in either settling the complaint for an exorbitant amount of money, returning the employee to work, and/or removing the disciplinary record. Again, the time of the investigation could be months which would disrupt the transportation company's operations. The longer the investigation took the more financially liable the company became and if the complaint could not be settled, it would be referred to an administrative law judge.

Hire the Right Staff Members

Larger companies ensure they have a sound safety program that includes the appropriate number of safety professionals to cover their areas of operations. In some cases, the safety staff can include a manager, assistants, safety specialists, and environmentalists. There may even be an in-house fire crew.

Medium and smaller companies tend to task other department heads such as the human resources manager, plant manager, or their assistants with covering the duties and responsibilities of the safety manager. Based on my experience, when the responsibilities are assigned to someone other than a dedicated safety professional, the program will not be effective. Department managers usually wear several different hats while doing their job. Adding "safety management" to their plate sets your company up for consequences ranging from injured personnel to financial ruin. Safety is not a part-time job: it's an everyday, all-day commitment.

The safety manager is a critical member of every other department in the company. The question posed to you as the leader is: Would you put your sanitation engineer over your financial department? If you answered no, then why would you put an unqualified member of your company to oversee the most critical component of your business? Having a seasoned safety professional creates stability, which in turn creates strength, empowerment, and consistency—which a safety program needs.

Hiring a safety professional can be a costly proposition, but not having a seasoned safety professional can cost your company millions — yes, millions. Injuries alone cost companies hundreds of thousands based on the type and number of injuries each year. Your safety professional manages your entire business by interacting with all departments, monitoring compensation cases, and being the point person for outside agencies such as EPA, Local Emergency Planning Committee (LEPC), OSHA, and other civic organizations.

Safety must be a core, active component of your business model. When was the last time you as the CEO walked with your safety professional throughout your facility? When was the last time you looked at your operation and evaluated and understood the importance of safety through the eyes of a professional? When you do this, it will catch the attention of your executive staff, supervisors, and employees.

While in the Federal Bureau of Prisons I had the opportunity to work with many Wardens and Associate Wardens who found the value in walking with me during my inspections or during their weekly tours. They felt it was an opportunity for staff and inmates alike to voice concerns and actually discuss the operation conducted within the food service area, UNICOR factories, healthcare, VT program, and even in the Powerhouse operations.

For those of you who might not be familiar with UNICOR it is the trade name for Federal Prison Industries (FPI) which is a wholly owned, self-sustaining Government corporation that sells market-priced services and quality goods made by inmates. The UNICOR factories are listed below:

- **Clothing and Textiles** from military clothing to mattresses, towels, linens, and screen printing.

- **Office Furniture** full spectrum of products to furnish reception areas, lounge areas, dormitory settings, medical offices, to executive suites.
- **Industrial Products** range from agency seals, traffic signs, vehicle tags, lockers, pallets, catwalks, prescription eyewear, and promotional products.
- **Electronics** range from cable assemblies, wire harnesses, circuit boards, and plastics/molding technologies.
- **Recycling** eight centers to recycle obsolete and excess electronics from both private and public sectors.
- **Fleet Solutions** provides a complete range of fleet modernization and remanufacturing programs to include tactical vehicle and vehicular components manufacturing.

As you can see, the staff and inmates working in these facilities have tremendous exposure in the equipment (power presses, tenon machines, edge banders, sanding machines, jointers, metal cutting, chemical, weight of cable roles, Humvees, loads of textile, warehouse operations, and forklift operations) being utilized in an around prison locations.

Just think of the amount of safety training required to complete these tasks. If we didn't invest the time in properly training and having oversight, the number of serious injuries could be insurmountable and the cost devastating, not to mention the reputation of UNICOR. So, let me ask you is safety an investment or a cost? If it wasn't for the fact that the Federal Bureau of Prisons saw the value in developing, maintaining, and hiring safety professionals due to the extraordinary work being performed by inmates and staff, these safety plans could have been cut and people could have been injured.

Safety is an investment.

When I first started my company, Safety By Design Consultant Service, I had a contractor by the name of Greg Bloskey come to my open house. He pulled me to the side and asked, "How many employees do I need to have to ensure their safety?" I replied, "If you have one employee, you're responsible for that life." Safety is expensive and so is a life.... Today he has two employees, and we talk about their safety weekly.

When your safety professionals speak, it should be known that they are speaking on your behalf when addressing company safety issues. Safety should be a critical component of every employee's performance assessment. Accountability must start at the top, A commitment to your investment in safety means that safety takes priority over everything yes, including production.

Your investment should include providing enough safety staff, resources, and funding to cover the hours of operation. If you only invest in one safety manager and you're operating three full shifts, what are you telling the employees on the other two shifts? What is your solution for the employees on the other two shifts? As a trainer, I always expound on the fact that one safety professional cannot manage an entire facility, especially with three eight-hour shifts. Safety is managed on the floor, and there is an enormous amount of administrative paperwork that needs to be completed.

Take, for example, Alcoa in 2012–13. They made safety their top priority, implementing a program called, "Stop for Safety." They had their best financial year ever, with the program reducing injuries and hence days missed because of those injuries.

At the end of 2013, 84.2 percent of Alcoa's safety reporting units had worked twelve consecutive months without a lost work- day, 49.5 percent without a DART (Days Away Restricted or Transferred) incident, and 42.4 percent without a total recordable incident.

The costs of not investing in safety range from OSHA fines, legal fees, preventable injuries and fatalities, loss of potential revenue, hazards to the community, loss of future business, and even prison time. Take a minute to close your eyes and focus on the faces of your employees. How would you feel if they were severely injured, maimed for life, or died in a work-related injury? How would their family members feel? How would you explain that?

What would that cost be? What if that injury or fatality could have been prevented by investing in a well-constructed safety program led by a seasoned safety professional? Now you tell me: Is safety a cost or an investment?

When employees were injured, when I was with the Bureau of Prisons it was extremely hard to speak with the family members. In some cases, the husband was the only source of income. You knew it was going to be a struggle, especially with families that had more than one child and additional responsibilities.

For example, my neighbor, an iron worker with two small children and a wife was recently injured at work. He fell from a height of 18 feet, and despite wearing a harness, was told not to hook in (secure to an anchor point that would support 5,000 pounds per employee). If he was tied off/hooked in he would not have suffered the injuries he sustained including bruises, cuts and other injuries from head to toe on one side of his body. He also had a torn pec muscle and was off work for an extended period of time. The harness was just for show he stated. He was lucky to be alive.

As I do the OSHA 10–30-hour trainings, I tell those in attendance there is not an employer that is paying you enough money to take a short cut or get injured; if they are, I want to be hired. The point being there is no amount of money that will take care of your family for you to get injured.

Investing in your employees' safety means you're investing in the faces of safety you may never see; family members you will never know. Can you put a price tag on that?

CHAPTER 2

The Price Tag

Safety isn't expensive, it's priceless.

How can anyone put a price tag on the lives of their employees? It happens every day in business. It's the bottom line that obscures the reality of what is important to every company, large or small. A question CEOs, CFOs, or anyone owning a business should ask themselves daily is: If my spouse, family member, or friend were working here, did I do everything I could to protect them? Your answer may surprise you, however, your actions may say something completely different.

I've been in small businesses where they valued their employees, and although they may not have had a tremendous amount of money, they did all they could to protect those who made them who they are. For example, we had several small companies that had 10-20 employees. They needed some guidance in establishing safety programs to protect their investments. We came in and conducted and evaluation and then set up a program that included monthly inspections, safety talks, and then monthly and or quarterly training. The most important aspect of this process was building a relationship with management and the employees so the latter could have a voice in safety related matters. For some of the clients we had it was about educating their employees on safe work procedures. This could range from how to read a safety data sheet to inspecting electrical cords, what personal protective equipment should be worn, and how to properly wear it.

Yes, the simplest exercise is asking someone how they put on ear plugs. Some just shove them into their ears, and others just barley have them in. When you demonstrate how to actually put them in there amazed at the difference in the sound. I had a CEO do this in training and he was definitely one we converted.

On the other hand, I've worked with companies who had all the money at their disposal and chose to gamble with the lives of their employees instead of protecting them. What a contrast. What a travesty to allow the safety of your employees to be tagged with the cost of their lives. Yes, we worked with several construction and manufacturing companies. They would say, "Train our employees, but we cannot have our hands tied down. Don't make any promises that we will have to keep or get the necessary or even required equipment."

We had one company tell their employees, "We can't afford to have any accidents, but we can't afford you to make work an all-day event to be safe."

I then worked at a restaurant, where it was known that I was a safety professional. I asked about their emergency plans. I knew just from being hired that they didn't have a great training program for either employee safety or food safety. They had many slips, trips, and fall injuries, due to the excess water on the floor, oil/grease on the floor, and then cardboard boxes on top of that. They had employees standing on wooden chairs filling up buckets of ice, then stepping down on that wet greasy floor. When we finally got to the point where I spoke with one of the regional managers, she pulled out a wet and dirty pamphlet of information. I asked, "So this is what you would pull out in case of an emergency, fire, accident." She stated, "Yes." I couldn't believe it. They never had any training on any of the safety items listed but they swore by that pamphlet.

All businesses operate somewhat like casinos: it's the house's money, and we'll always win more than we lose. If we have an injury or fatality, that is the cost of doing business. Instead of repairing a missing machine guard, addressing an electrical malfunction, or replacing an unsafe ladder, the company turns its head until someone gets hurt. Once this happens, the fingers begin to point. The only difference is three fingers pointing back at them. Could that be you?

It's sad that some companies place more value on giving corporate bonuses than on protecting and investing in their employees. I've actually had a CEO of a prominent restaurant chain in Kentucky tell me that I was completely correct in my safety assessment of their organization and that he would hire me to create more safety awareness. My assessment was that they lacked initial training, no emergency drills, no appropriate PPE for the work they were doing, and sanitation was at a minimal level to say the least. However, he decided to use the funds to provide corporate bonuses instead of investing in his restaurant and their employees. I then asked him what would happen if one or more of his employees died in a fire because they didn't know how to respond. He simply looked at me and said that was why he carried insurance.

I was so upset to hear that the lives of his employees throughout these restaurants have a value reduced to that of an insurance policy. At that point, I wished him all the best and added that I couldn't believe that his employees weren't worth more than the value of an insurance policy.

However, he wasn't the only CEO of a large company that had this attitude. The employees who perform the tasks to make their companies thrive are only worth an insurance policy. That's criminal. The price tag of life goes way beyond the value of one person. What about the faces that will never be seen? The spouse, the parent, the child, the baby on the way... What are their lives worth?

Do we understand the effect safety has on the company, the coworker, the family, and friends?

Believe it or not, there is a price tag for every part of the human body; this is multiplied by an abstract number of weeks to determine how much an employee can receive for that injury and even the employee's family for a fatality.

The price tag for safety was a simple machine guard that wasn't in place, but the employee was required to operate the piece of equipment to get the product out the door. Then, tragedy struck, and the employee was severely injured. The cost to repair or replace that guard was $30.00 but the cost of the preventable injury was $50,000, not to mention the pain and suffering, as well as the family and work functions missed. You can put a price tag on treating the injury, but there is no way to calculate what that injury cost the worker's family: their pain, their suffering, and maybe even the loss of their loved one.

Even today you see utility workers exposing themselves by being in trenches over their heads with no protection whatsoever. While a safety manager with the Bureau of Prisons, I was involved in a sewer line project. I was required to go over the safety requirements of our facility prior to the contract work commencing. While inspecting the sewer line project, I noticed that the contractors had a trench approximately 4-6 feet wide, and 15-20 feet deep. One of them was in the bottom of this pit, with an excavator in excess of 10+ tons straddling the trench, as rocks were being poured into it. The employee had no exits points and no ladder. I noticed that the sides of the trench were beginning to collapse. At this point, I halted the operation, had the employee removed from the trench and advised the contractor that they were out of the scope of our safety policies. After I halted this project, which was costing our facility thousands of dollars, the warden requested that I be sent home. After being sent home I returned the next day.

The warden and I walked around, he actually told me, "If you want to work in a safe environment, then you need to work somewhere else." I explained that I had the responsibility of protecting his ass and the institution and that what they were doing could have created a trench collapse. The next day, I encountered the same, I took some pictures, called a friend of mine working in OSHA and he stated that is a willful violation since I advised them of the same issue the day before. The warden found out that I sent the pictures and memos written to OSHA. He then had a teleconference with my friend and the warden sent out a message that all contract activities regarding the sewer line project must adhere to all OSHA standards and our local safety policies.

The only thing they cared about was the cost of the delay. This said a lot about who we were as an organization. I was appalled that money was more important than the lives of those who could have been injured or killed because safety was not a business priority.

Where are our morals when it comes to protecting the lives of our employees? Are employee's expendable? Are their families any less important? The warden should have been held accountable for the employees and contract personnel he was responsible for. It appears that the cost of the project had a price tag more valuable than the lives that project could have taken.

As a CEO, CFO, executive staff member, or supervisor, when was the last time you told your employees how important they are? How valuable they are to the success of the company, their department, community, and most of all their families?

When an employee has a fatal injury do you participate in the funeral, meet the family get a better understanding of who your employee was, or do you just send a representative and never think about it again? Remember that the lives of your employees and the faces of safety can never be valued with a price tag. Safety: you just can't afford not to have it. Many lives depend on it.

CHAPTER 3

Seconds

You only have so much time to Stop! Think! Then Act!

Seconds. That's how long it takes for the consequences of a decision you make to become everlasting. Think about it. We make decisions every day, every hour, every minute that could change our lives, the lives of our coworkers, the lives of our employees, and the lives of our families.

How many times have you walked through your home and seen a situation that just didn't look right? However, instead of deciding to eliminate a potential hazard, you continued to walk on and not think any more about it. For example, how many times do we leave our shoes on the stairs, knowing it's a tripping hazard and someone is going to take a fall and could sustain a broken arm, head injury, or even a hip injury.

How many times when we're cooking, or boiling water do we leave the handles to our pots and pans exposed to where they can be hit or knocked over where someone is going to get severely burned. Just imagine one of your toddlers reaching up for the handle and they're scalded by the hot water, grease, and or food. How would you feel knowing that accident could have been prevented if you just paid attention.

Here is another example. How many of us are storing gasoline in a cheap plastic gas container with no flash arresting screen and a spring closing lid. We store them in the garage on the floor next to our vehicles and then we start the cars. Or we run out of gas cutting the lawn and we open the tank and start pouring gas into the lawn mower while it is very hot which could lead to the fuel igniting and serious burns, possibly an explosion. But we do this every summer, and we don't think about the burns, Why? Because we've been lucky. One day, our luck is going to runout and the burns will be everlasting scars to remind us.

A situation like this is actually a bomb waiting to explode. It's suggested that you wait at least 5 minutes after you run out of gas to refill your lawn mower or even put additional oil into the lawn mower. Never do either one while the lawn mower is running. To view the exploding gas container, you can go to https://youtube.be-YWV2GFvc8M Chanel 2 WBS-TV.

One summer in Louisiana, I witnessed a woman put a small plastic gas container in her car after filling it up. She proceeded to get into her vehicle and lit a cigarette. Her car burst into flames. The scene was devastating but not as eerie as her screams for help.

Tomorrow, you will go to work. You're the president of the company; your responsibility is to provide a safe and healthy workplace, and to protect the employees who walk through your door. You ask your executive assistant to bring you the last safety inspection reports. She asks why the interest, and why now.

These are the reports you've had your assistant file with no action, no intervention, and no desire to get involved. You begin to read them, shake your head, place notes on them, and then finally realize that you have not held yourself accountable for the lives and well-being of every manager, supervisor, and employee.

Then, you decide to set some expectations, realizing that you've placed the lives of your employees, as well as the future of your company, at risk. But before you can get started, an alarm goes off. Chaos takes over. An employee has been fatally injured. He was pulled into an auger that was not properly guarded.

Time is of the essence when lives are in the balance. How much time does it really take to save a life?

Production has been on the rise and this piece of equipment couldn't be properly maintained due to the shortage of staff and the lack of safety supervision. The employee was thirty-five years old with a spouse and three small children.

You recall overhearing conversations from several employees about the lack of safety and how maintenance was not a priority. You go back to the inspection reports and note that there have been several near misses in this same area.

As the hours move forward, the day of the funeral takes the company in an entirely new direction. Employees are emotionally moved, and grief-stricken, as families come together and mourn the loss of a young man who was trying to make a living for his family.

Seconds have turned into a slow-motion movie featuring a tragedy that could have been prevented. There is nothing you can say. Your heart is full of sorrow, your mind keeps retracing all your steps: the lack of accountability on your part is killing you inside.

When you look at his family, you see the faces you've never thought about: his wife and their three small children. How are they going to move forward? Did he have enough life insurance? Do they have any illnesses? Do they have other family to help them? How are they going to make it through this tragic event? These are the unseen faces of safety that will struggle for eternity.

Lee Shelby

I have a friend, a coworker who suffered a tragic work-related event in his life. His name is Lee Shelby. He has a tremendous story that will touch hearts, save lives, and move families. He will never forget the seconds that turned his life completely upside down.

Lee was an electrical lineman and had been doing this work for some twelve years or more. One day, Lee was on a job, disconnecting wires from a residence. He clipped the first two wires and repositioned his hands to clip the third. When he did, 13,200 volts of electricity ran through his body. He fell inside the bucket. Co-workers took his gloves off and found that his skin was completely fried and immediately rushed him to the hospital.

Lee has endured some very emotional and heartbreaking events from the time he suffered his injury. His hands and arms were so badly burned and damaged that doctors removed both hands and arms to his elbows, then fitted him with prosthetics. He spent a significant time in the burn unit. Imagine the pain, the loss of both arms, and never again being able to do the things he loved: his job, his future, and income.

In the beginning, the pain, suffering, uncertainty, and hospital stays were just too much for his entire family to endure. His injury led the love of his life to divorce him on top of everything else he was going through.

As time went on, Lee got remarried; however, to this day, he has never been able to touch the skin of his wife, hold her hand, caress her, or play ball with his grandson who is the light of his world. Lee is an avid athlete and he had been his grandson's biggest cheerleader and advocate.

Yes, even today Lee feels the effects of his injury. There is no amount of money he can make that will replace what he could have done with his hands and arms. Having to hold things with his prosthetic claws instead of touching things with his hands and fingers. He lost the ability to do the most simple and enjoyable things in his life like throwing a baseball with his grandson, working out with weights, driving, and simple household tasks. His passion for life is expressed in his safety presentations and he is driven to make sure that his injury never happens to anyone else.

Could his injury have been prevented? Yes, and Lee openly admits that if he had had the appropriate personal protective equipment (PPE), things might have been different. Instead, seconds changed his entire life. Lee Shelby's story is detailed in, *Workplace Safety Is Not Optional; Triumph over Tragedy; Consequences.*

There are many faces of safety in this story, faces that will remain nameless: parents, children, grandchildren, neighbors, church family, friends, and coworkers. As I said earlier, his story can and will save lives. Please go to his website, leeshelby.com and have Lee come to your company to share his story.

Seconds Matter

Seconds are all we have to make decisions that will have a tremendous impact. Many lives depend on these decisions. In emergencies, medical, fire, gas releases, or inclement weather, seconds could be the difference between life and death.

I have a client that had an employee sever a hand on a press that delivers 1,000 to 3,000 pounds of force per square inch. The employee accidently leaned forward as he was teaching another employee how to operate the press. When he did so, he extended his arm, placing his hand into the press, and accidently stepped on the unguarded foot pedal. The staff immediately called 911, and although the fire department and ambulance service were only minutes away it took 18 minutes before they arrived and provided medical treatment. During this time, the employee could have bled out as they didn't have any medical personnel on staff. He lost his hand.

How many times have you, as a supervisor, walked through your area, seen an employee doing something unsafe, for example standing on the top step of a ladder, operating a power press without operational light curtains, blocking an exit door with a forklift, and chosen not to say a word? What do you think your employees thought? Those actions you took spoke volumes although you didn't say a word. The behavior we walk past is the behavior we accept. So, when that employee is injured and he goes to his attorney, he will say my supervisor passed me several times and never told me to step down off that ladder, don't use that press until we get the light curtains repaired, or remove that forklift front in front of the exit door. The attorney will say, "He never said anything to you or never documented your actions?" The reply will simply be, "No." What do you think will happen next?

We laugh when it comes to conducting fire drills. But as a firefighter, it's not a laughing matter, especially when you have recovered bodies lying right in front of an exit—people who didn't make it out. Every second counts and the faces of safety matter, if not to you, to someone they loved.

As a Fire Chief, EMT, and Firefighter I-II certified by the State of California I ran a fire crew out of the Mojave Desert (Federal Prison Camp) Boron, CA. We received a call from San Bernardino County of a vehicle roll over with three passengers. We responded to this call in a matter of 5 minutes. When I arrived on scene there were two toddlers and a mother. They were lying on the hot desert ground. The bodies were placed in a triangle. My squad of five inmates, evaluated the scene. It appeared that the bodies were ejected from the car due to the high desert winds that day. The mother was DOA and one toddler on the right of her mother was also DOA. I positioned my body in-between the surviving toddler (little girl) and her mother trying to shield her from seeing her mother. She kept crying, asking to see her mom. I tried to reassure the young girl that everything was going to be okay. The other inmate EMT's performed CPR on the other sister with unfavorable results. I was fighting back my own tears and emotions, knowing that this little girl just lost her sister and mother. I had to gather myself and determine that if this little girl had a chance, I need to request a medivac as her injuries were critical and time was of the essence.

It seemed like forever before the helicopter arrived. It was my first time ever landing in a helicopter. My heart was racing: deep inside I was shaking because the little girl only had a certain amount of time and that was on my shoulders. We landed and packaged the young girl for transport. After she was removed from the scene and we returned to the federal prison camp, we all were an emotional state. I had to call my kids in Kentucky and let them know every time they were in the car, they needed to wear their seatbelts. I sobbed like a baby.

I went to the hospital at least two days during the next few weeks, holding the young girl, pushing her in a wagon on the floor as she slept. It was so heart wrenching to know this child lost her sister and her mother. One of the nurses asked if I was her father. I said, "No. She was a call that I responded to and I was in charge of treating her at the scene." I remember to this day the split-second decisions that were made to try and save this family. Tragically, lives were lost, and a young girl will grow up without her sister and her mother.

To this day, when I think about this little girl (now a woman), tears fill my eyes and pain touches my heart and hope is all I can pray for that this woman is living a healthy life and we has something to do with that.

How many of us reading this book are trained and ready to respond to a medical emergency? Your spouse, neighbor, coworker, or God forbid, your child has stopped breathing ... what do you do? Life and death are only separated by seconds: could you save the life of someone you love?

We touch a thousand lives every day, but are we prepared to make a difference? It takes seconds to reach out a hand and pull someone out of a dangerous situation, seconds to tell your coworker they are not safe, seconds to respond to someone who has stopped breathing, and seconds to tell the those you love how much you care. Tomorrow is not promised. Every second of your life counts.

In Remembrance

The faces of safety are in your hands. What will you do when seconds matter?

If you want a reminder of the lives that are lost on a daily basis, then go to OSHA's website, remembrance@dol.gov. There is a virtual Workers Memorial Wall in honor of those who lost their lives while on the job. In addition to injuries or incidents, there have been many lives lost due to occupational illnesses and diseases in the U.S. They are family members — spouses, children, siblings, grandparents, friends, and coworkers — and we recognize them and all our fallen workers on this page. This page was developed in partnership with the United Support & Memorial for Workplace Fatalities (USMWF).

Now that you understand how seconds can make a difference, think about the importance of being proactive instead of reactive and what that could mean to your company, employees, family, and friends.

CHAPTER 4

Reactive vs. Proactive

Fix the safety issues today so your employees can have a safer tomorrow.

"Let's just cuddle on the couch tonight and watch a movie. I'll send the kids to their grandma's so we can have some quiet time together. I love you, Candiss."

Why do we wait until someone is injured or killed before we decide to do the right thing? As a safety professional, I struggle to understand the rationale behind this type of thinking. My only conclusion is that either we don't have the foresight to see what is about to happen, or we simply don't care, and either way, that's a shame.

We walk through our facilities, we travel through construction zones, we hold meetings and discuss projects, maintenance issues, and safety concerns. However, once the meeting is concluded ... nobody seems to care. It's just words without impact or follow-up. That is, until something happens, a fire, accident, fatality, or OSHA comes knocking at the door.

Then, when something goes pear-shaped, which simply means it didn't turn out the way it was expected to, so you scrap it, and lives are ruined, it's a little too late to try to be proactive. What prevents someone from standing up and saying, *"Enough is Enough?"* Is it money, authority, expectations, responsibilities, or lack thereof? We're no longer going to stand by and put our employees at risk by being complacent. Every executive staff member, supervisor, and employee is going to be held accountable for the safety and well-being of their coworkers, their managers, and everyone who walks through the door.

Reactively is how most companies respond when incidents like those mentioned above take place. Yes, we knew the hazard existed; however, we decided to wait, to play the game of chance. The problem with the game of chance is it often costs the life of an employee. What a price tag. We know that being reactive costs more than if we just take care of the issue or hazard in the first place. How many more lives need to be taken, families burdened, and children left parentless?

I know and understand that companies struggle financially, but is that a reason to ignore hazards? How many companies have dedicated safety personnel to monitor what I believe is a critical component of any company? How can we be proactive when we have CEOs, CFOs, and executives that have no understanding of the functions, responsibilities, and value that a safety professional brings to a company?

Responding reactively to maintenance issues, especially when the efficiency of your operations depends on the equipment operating properly, is a recipe for disaster. I've worked for several companies that failed to have enough qualified maintenance staff and electricians to make sure the equipment is in peak operating condition. You have machine operators who think and believe that they are qualified to perform maintenance on their equipment. This could lead to potential injuries and maybe even a fatality. You have machine operators on the second and third shifts that need to have their equipment operating, and if it's not, they may take matters into their own hands. I've seen operators try and repair the equipment they are working on only to be shocked by a jolt of electricity, since they didn't lockout/tagout the equipment. Have they been authorized to do this work under the Control of Hazardous Energy (Lockout/Tagout) 29 CFR 1910.147?

I have seen a qualified electrician do work on a switch panel without using a double insulated tool. (Portable electric tools are constructed with a special insulating system in lieu of a grounding means.) These tools need to be inspected prior to each use and must comply with the National Electrical Code. The tool came in contact with the electrical system, shocking his body and causing him to flop around like a fish. If the tool was properly insulated, he could have avoided being shocked.

I've seen untrained forklift operators move pallets of items and had near misses with employees walking in their way due to being distracted. Forklifts are 3,000 -20,000-pound pieces of equipment, powerful and heavy enough, to kill, impale, and even knock down a complete storage racking system. The forks can easily penetrate the body of another employee, or slice into a 55-gallon drum of chemicals. I've seen forklift operators become lethargic and dizzy, with severe headaches because they were operating in an area that was not properly ventilated, and/or the propane cylinder had a leak.

Carbon monoxide and carbon dioxide are specific hazards when propane-powered equipment is used in an enclosed, poorly ventilated area. The gas is stored under pressure, and is flammable when mixed with air, making leaks very dangerous as it could create an explosion or fire. Propane leaks under extreme conditions could lead to convulsions, coma, and possible death.

Another example is when forklift operators are loading trailers unaware of the floor damage and weight conditions of the trailer they are loading. Thus, a forklift could fall through the floor, or the driver could move his/her trailer without the operator knowing it until it falls out of the trailer, maiming the operator, damaging product and property. Again, nothing happens until it affects the bottom line ... but then it is too late. The injuries have occurred, lives are changed forever. How do you react to that?

If we would have taken the time to make that repair, we wouldn't have to be visiting the burn unit and seeing the tears on the faces of the family members.

We have a lot of non-safety professionals trying to do jobs that are extremely complex. There are a number of environmental and safety programs such as the Clean Water Act, Tier I-II Reporting, Storm Water, Respiratory Protection, Lockout/Tagout, Confined Spaces/Permit Required Confined Spaces, PPE Assessments, and Machine Guarding to consider just to name a few. How can you react to an incident when you have no knowledge of the safety issues and specific legal requirements? It's like placing a sanitation engineer as your CFO. It's something that you just wouldn't do.

Let's face it, HR manager is full-time position with tremendous legal ramifications. Plant manager is another position that is extremely complex and involves a few very skilled and technical staff members. Their focus is on the entire operation of the facility.

However, as a safety professional, I've been through manufacturing, textile, cable, power press, furniture, automotive, food processing, fabricating, welding, woodworking, RV manufacturing, utility, powerhouse, and health-care facilities, and the lack of safety oversight by qualified professionals is alarming. Who would take charge if a fire, workplace violence, explosion, chemical release, or medical emergency were to occur?

It's time to be proactive in every sense of the word. Proactivity demonstrates ownership, accountability, responsibility, and that you value the lives of your employees and those who may enter your facility. Monitoring and following up on safety equipment and procedures will reduce the potential for injury or loss of life.

Companies are exposed to many different scenarios that could be devastating to their business. Proactively providing their employees with a safe work environment is an OSHA requirement. It's not only the law; it's the right thing to do. We spend so much time trying to do the opposite of what we should be doing that we take the focus from what is important.

Being proactive means providing the necessary staff, resources, and training to ensure all employees are protected. It means taking those resources, providing expectations, and holding management, supervisors, and employees accountable. If we take the time to show our employees that they're not just a number or a body, but that they're important and valuable members of our companies, we can make a tremendous impact not only in productivity but in reducing injuries and reducing complaints, all by making safety a core value in our daily activities.

The value of being proactive can create a financial windfall for companies. Looking forward, identifying needs, and managing by walking around can be substantial, especially if your facility is large, has lots of equipment, or lacks the appropriate number of safety staff.

By walking around, you see things in a different light: maintenance issues, shipping concerns, productivity, morale, and how things are being managed by supervisors. As the CEO, taking time to walk through your business indicates that you have control and that you want to make sure things are moving according to the information provided or discussed in meetings. It speaks volumes when you have a positive and direct hand in what is taking place.

Management walkthroughs have been very effective in the past when times were supposedly simpler. In our world today, being proactive could mean being caught in the state of technology, not sure if that is a good thing or not. We're not talking, we're writing emails, texting, and avoiding critical conversations that need to happen. This is why being proactive in face-to-face communication is so important to the success of your business. When was the last time you had a conversation with an employee and heard what he or she said? Think about that.

It's kind of like that old Midas commercial: pay me now or pay me later, but you will pay me. It's so much easier and cost-effective to make sound financial investments in your company on maintenance, preventative maintenance, and appropriate staffing.

Knowing how vital certain management positions are and the value they bring to your company can bring insight into critical business decisions.

Being proactive is a positive attribute for your company. It could bring a windfall of business; however, the commitment to safety will be the key influence businesses want to see, as this commitment reflects your passion, involvement, and sincerity to your employees—and that speaks volumes.

CHAPTER 5

A Commitment to Safety

Are we committed or not...If so, safety must be a core value?

"I just want you to know how important you are to me and the kids. We need you and most of all we love you."

Commitment. What is it, what does it mean to your business, and how important is it to the success of your future? A commitment to safety speaks volumes without you as the CEO, CFO, executive staff member, or supervisor ever speaking a single word.

Commitment to safety means that you've invested in your employees, that you've made sure your top priority is to protect those who make your business all it can be. We tend to forget who makes the business function today, tomorrow, and in the future, it's your employees.

A commitment is a powerful statement, but unless you have taken the corresponding actions, it has no value. When the CEO promotes safety by their actions, then a message has been sent from the top down. As a safety professional, I have always tried to get the CEO to be active in the inspection process, safety committee meetings, and even just simple walkthroughs of an area with a member of their safety team.

The impression this gives shows all department heads that the safety team has authority and accountability set forth by the CEO/CFO. The walkthrough and interactions during this activity say that when the safety staff speaks, they are communicating on the leadership team's behalf.

Commitment to safety *must* include expectations and accountability. The CEO must establish clear expectations of the executive management team, mid-level management teams, and supervisors for all levels.

These expectations must also be placed in their performance evaluations to comprehensively demonstrate the company's commitment to safety.

The expectations should include the following:

- Clearly and effectively communicate safety issues.
- Provide oversight and follow through on outstanding safety issues until they are resolved.
- Promote the value and importance of safety to all levels of management.
- Make sure all levels of supervisors and employees know the commitment of upper management.
- Participate in departmental walk-throughs to demonstrate commitment to the safety team.
- Conduct informal walk-throughs and listen to staff members' safety concerns.
- Follow up on all outstanding items identified in the walk-throughs.

If the expectations are clear and you hold yourself, executive management, supervisors, and employees accountable, then everyone will understand your commitment to this program. However, if you are not consistent in accountability, your safety program will be ineffective, creating confusion, discontent, lower morale, reduced productivity, and the risk of fines and legal fees.

Accountability. It's what I stress in all my training classes. If the CEO, CFO, or members of the executive staff are not holding their employees accountable, they only have themselves to blame. Accountability is a critical component of each member's performance evaluation. How can you not hold your employees accountable if you expect your business to be successful?

Sure, it takes time and effort to monitor your employees' actions. Everyone has responsibilities on their plate, but in the long run, accountability is crucial. How can you evaluate, counsel, write up, or even terminate an employee if they don't know the expectations you have established for them in terms of safety? You can't.

Try to hold your executive management staff, supervisors, and employees accountable if they have no understanding of their expectations. The two of these go hand in hand to create your commitment to safety. It's like requesting your employees to write their own evaluations. What are you telling them when you ask them to do this? *Let me answer.* You either don't know enough about what they've done, or you're too lazy to take the time to write an evaluation. Most employees want to be recognized for their efforts. If you cannot provide them with a raise or a bonus, then take the time necessary to write an evaluation that is worth reading and says something significant about their work performance and their commitment to safety.

As the supervisor, CEO, or CFO, wouldn't you expect the same thing, or does it not matter to you as long as you receive that bonus check? I believe we forget how to tell our employees about the value they bring to our companies. When you write an evaluation in a small box that contains twenty-five to thirty-two characters, what are you telling your employees? Can you expound on their commitment to safety?

Safety without expectations, accountability, or commitment will have a tremendous impact on your business. Most people expect to have expectations and be held accountable in some form or fashion. However, with the pressures of business, how much commitment can be given to safety before it creates a battle between safety, production, and quality?

Your commitment to safety includes touching the lives of every family member. We don't realize how safety at work affects every member of every family. Maybe if we did, commitment to safety as a core value would be higher on the list. When was the last time one of your employees was injured? Did you ever check on their emotional status? Financial well-being? If not, maybe that is a procedure that needs to be implemented. The family members of our employees are just as important as the employees. These are the faces of safety that no one seems to care about. They contribute so much to the company in ways that are unmeasurable.

If your employee's family status is consistent, with no devastating issues such as divorce, sickness, family discord, or financial or school problems, they are most likely a sound employee. But how would you as the employer know that if you've never taken the time to get involved with your people, especially the ones who have been injured on the job?

One significant injury, or worse, the loss of a life, means we need to reevaluate our commitment to safety. When we say, "commitment to safety," it should include resources, staffing, funding, and a public commitment by the CEO.

Today, most CEOs, COOs, and other executive members have no real concept of the responsibilities and liabilities that come with managing a safety program. No matter how large or how small the company is, safety should be a core element of every company's business model.

If you're a CEO or other business executive, you could be held personally liable for actions taken by your company. Leaders can be held personally responsible for debts, or criminally liable for illegal or non-compliant activities, even without your direct knowledge.

Multiple former executives of a now closed e-scrap (i.e., old or worn-out electronic devices) have been sentenced to serve prison time for violations of US hazardous waste storage and management regulations.

In March of 2022, an individual who served as EH&S Director, Operations Manager, and Executive VP at the company was sentenced to five months in Federal prison for "conspiracy to store and transport hazardous waste without the required permits and manifests," according to a DOJ press release.

The company managed glass from broken and crushed cathode ray tubes or CRTs at facilities in Wisconsin and Tennessee. Because the CRT glass contained lead, it met EPA's definition of a hazardous waste and was subject to the Resource Conservation and Recovery Act (RCRA).

RCRA violations that led to criminal enforcement in this case included:

- Knowingly storing hazardous waste at unpermitted facilities;
- Knowingly shipping or transporting hazardous waste without a required manifest; and
- Concealing violations from state regulator and auditors.

Employees tried to conceal the hazardous waste violations by changing the dates on containers and providing fraudulent inventory and shipping records to state regulators. The facilities also hid hazardous waste containers in semi-trailers, behind pallets, and in a warehouse kept secret from inspectors.

The five-month prison sentence is the latest in a string of criminal enforcement actions against the company's executives. Late last year, the company's president was sentenced to 18 months in prison for criminal hazardous waste violations and tax-avoidance.

Not Every RCRA Violation is a Crime

Most of the time, violations of the RCRA hazardous waste regulations do not result in prison time, but the monetary penalties for these violations increase every year, up to $70,000 per day, per violation.

Safety affects every aspect of a business. So then, why it is so damn difficult to make safety a critical component and core value is beyond me. When CEOs talk about the bottom line, safety needs to be in that discussion. A lack of commitment to safety causes injuries, deaths, liabilities, OSHA, and EPA fines, and affects the bottom line.

A commitment to safety can and will enhance the bottom line by increasing quality and productivity and reducing lost man-hours, overtime costs, training costs, long-term medical payments, and insurance premiums.

Alcoa CEO, Paul O'Neill: The Value of Safety in Manufacturing

Driven by the philosophy that putting profits over people is "always a stupid idea," former Alcoa CEO, Paul O'Neill, proved that a lasting commitment to workplace safety must start at the top. Alcoa is an aluminum manufacturing giant where the metals are 1,500 degrees and machines are powerful enough to rip a man's arm off. In 1987, the aluminum giant was in a state of disarray. O'Neill presented a presentation to investors on what they thought was his new leadership move to reduce overhead, improve profits, and significantly raise the stock price. However, he began his speech by stating he was going to talk about worker safety.

The energy was completely sucked out of the room and there was silence. "He further stated every year, numerous Alcoa workers are injured so badly they miss a day of work," he then stated, "I intend to make Alcoa the safest company in America. I intend to go for zero injuries." He believes that an injury-free workplace "is a precondition not a priority." Alcoa's market value increased from $3 billion to $27 billion by focusing on one single habit: worker Safety. Focusing on workers safety can transform an organization and improve the culture, quality, productivity, and ultimately the bottom-line profits. Mr. O'Neill stated, "We're going to focus on safety over profits."

The reason Mr. O'Neill focused on safety was every time an employee was injured the time missed from work was days to weeks and even months creating issues with productivity. Alcoa has made a substantial drop from 1.86 lost workdays to 0.2 lost workdays per 100 employees.

"It's like breathing: You can't do much else if you don't remember to breathe pretty frequently," O'Neill said during a keynote address at the 2013 National Safety Congress and Expo in Chicago. We should have the same attitude toward the safety of our workforce.

O'Neill put his money where his mouth was. When the company's legal counsel fretted that displaying the names of injured employees would embolden tort lawyers "to sue the hell out of us," O'Neill pledged to pay any damages out of his own pocket.

"In the thirteen years I was there, there never was a lawsuit," O'Neill said. During his thirteen-year tenure, Alcoa's lost-workday rate dropped from 1.86 to 0.23, while its market value ballooned from $3 billion in 1986 to $27.5 billion in 2000. (As of Oct. 2, the company's lost-workday rate for 2013 stood at 0.085, according to Alcoa's website.)

Be Committed

Commitment's easier said than done. Commitment requires that everyone have the same vision, game plan, and direction. Safety is all well and good until the operations manager starts complaining that safety slows down productivity, but there is no alternative but to forge ahead.

Commitment means money and resources. The CFO says we need to make cuts, combine departments, reduce staffing, and there goes the safety department or manager. That's not a joke. Companies tend to see the safety manager as expendable, believing it will work to add safety responsibilities to the HR manager's functions to reduce costs.

The problem with this is that it doesn't work. It never has, and it never will. HR manager is a full-time position with tremendous administrative responsibilities. Safety, on the other hand, must be out on the floor.

The job of a safety manager is observing, monitoring, assisting employees, supporting management with oversight of the operations, engaging with the employees, identifying potential safety hazards, conducting inspections, and arranging training. Safety managers also aid HR with compensation cases and documentation to legal teams regarding environmental issues or OSHA complaints. Another responsibility of a safety manager is walking with the members of the fire department as they conduct inspections and testing on the fire alarm systems, including smoke alarms and sprinkler systems.

Safety is a 24/7 position with tremendous responsibility. Anything can happen at any time, and we must be committed to protecting every one of our employees. What is the perception of the employees who work evenings and mornings when we don't provide a safety professional on these shifts? What message are we sending? Do we place any value on those working the off shifts? Who's protecting their lives?

These are all great questions. As the CEO or COO, can you answer them? They are easy or difficult to answer based on your commitment.

I worked for a company, Panduit, that had several safety staff members and three local locations. Some of their facilities ran two or three shifts. As a new safety program manager, I was appalled when they stated there was no safety coverage for the other shifts. So, I decided that I would work the second and third shifts so I could evaluate what was going on.

My objective was to get to know the employees and demonstrate my genuine concern for their well-being. I wanted to know how they felt about safety, production, maintenance, and the commitment from the executive staff and their supervisors. My mission included hearing their concerns and suggestions regarding safety, injuries, productivity, and how we could have a positive effect together.

We should be as committed to the families that support our employees. Do, we even know their names?

I was told when I was first hired that safety was a core value to the company. However, when I dug a little deeper, safety was never mentioned in their core values. They recently had a third-party survey completed, and safety was never mentioned. At that point, I began to question their commitment to safety. It wasn't long after that when I discovered the bottom line was more important than the safety of their employees.

Commitment to safety was only evident in the signs that hung throughout their locations stating, "Safety First" and "Safety Is No Accident." The truth of the matter was safety wasn't first, second, or even third.

So, when I talk about commitment to safety, I expect commitment, not in words or on signs but in actions. For every one dollar invested in workplace safety, the return is four to six dollars, according to the National Safety Council.

Commitment is when you're all in and expectations are clear, when everyone from the CEO down is accountable for their actions, and when safety is a core value of the business.

A calculation for "sales equivalent dollars" is financial losses or savings multiplied by 100 percent, divided by the profit margin percentage. For example, if you wanted to know what a $10,000 injury would take in additional sales to make that money back, and your business' profit margin was 5 percent, you'd take $10,000 multiplied by 100 percent, divided by 5, which equals $200,000. Once management understands how hard getting $200,000 in sales is for your company, it can bring a whole new perspective to safety.

Safety enhances the opportunities to gain new business as well as to maintain current business relationships. It speaks volumes on how we manage our business and respect our clients, how we care for our employees and the community, and how we demonstrate that we're a business that protects its investments and its employees' futures.

Commitment to safety is exemplified when we focus on the family, the backbone of our business and our success. When one of our employees is injured, severely maimed, or killed it's our responsibility to step up and take care of their loved ones, for they were instrumental in taking care of us.

If you're committed to protecting the health and lives of your employees, you'll never question yourself on the value of safety and whether you can afford it.

CHAPTER 6

Safety: You Can't Afford Not to Have It

Safety is an insurance policy for the families left behind that we don't want them to cash.

"Honey, can you believe we're expecting our first baby? Please be careful at work, as I would die if something happened to you."

As a senior safety consultant, I've been in many small businesses where safety is not even a consideration. The reason is the cost. I have pleaded with many small business owners asserting that safety is not expendable. I want to make a positive impact on small-to-medium-sized businesses.

The cost of safety cannot and does not compare to the cost of a life, injuries, compensation costs, insurance premiums, OSHA fines, and civil suits—or the loss of business.

Does properly implementing safety cost? Sure, it does, but not having a solid safety program could cost you more than just money. Businesses are opting to utilize services like ISNetworld and AVETTA to upgrade their safety programs and review OSHA 300A logs to determine numbers of injuries and MOD rate (a multiplier for insurance premiums calculated based on the difference between a company's workers' compensation claims and those of comparable businesses).

ISNetworld is the global leader in contractor and supplier information management. Since 2001, ISNetworld has helped enterprises proactively reduce risk by qualifying and monitoring contractors to promote safe and sustainable operations throughout the supply chain. The all-inclusive and configurable subscription-based platform, **ISNetworld®**, helps companies identify the most qualified contractor companies that meet and exceed industry, regulatory, and company-specific standards in the areas of health, safety, quality, insurance, training, cybersecurity and ESG.

Companies that want to do business will take this information and use it to determine if you're worth the risk. I had several companies work through ISNetworld in which they had to create, update, and modify manuals and training programs. ISNetworld has an accountability to contractors and companies to ensure that they provide documentation to receive a grade based on number of injuries and lost workdays.

Avetta Description provides the foundation for clients, suppliers, contractors, workers, and vendors to forge stronger relationships, ensuring every workplace is safe and sustainable. We assist companies in identifying qualified contractors that would meet industry, regulatory, and company specific standards for safety.

We also combine our risk management tools, benchmarking data, and subject matter expertise to help you design and develop a supply chain risk management program that is aligned with your organizational goals and leads to optimal outcomes. Our team of subject matter experts with significant domain knowledge and operational experience, provide a consultative approach to solution your supply chain risk management needs. Additionally, we partner with our customers to assess their risk management program and develop solutions that are tailored to their specific need.

Small companies that only have one recordable injury in the last three years could be left out of the bidding process. This is a process that small companies believe is unfair. I worked with several small-business owners that fell into this category and were excluded from the process of winning a contract that could have made their company more sustainable.

As the previous owner of Safety By Design Consulting Services we had a welding/fabrication company that had a small number of employees, without any safety oversight. We assisted them by developing a monthly inspection program and training. Again, my company was trying to make safety affordable for small and medium size companies by creating a small monthly payment plan. The objective was to help promote safety among the employees and educate them through the inspection process. We helped management understand that their small investment creates positive dividends by reducing injuries and working with their insurance company to reduce premiums.

If you're a small-to-medium-sized business with between ten and fifty employees, and you have reduced expenses by having your HR manager also be responsible for safety, what you've created is an unsafe workplace for your employees.

I've run into several small-to-medium-sized companies that have hired inexperienced safety professionals and have created a monstrosity of problems. The administrative side of safety has a tremendous amount of legal liabilities. Why would you want to expose your company to those issues and/or concerns?

Most HR or plant managers will be honest and say they spend maybe 5 percent of their time dealing with safety operations. Their business is personnel issues and productivity, not safety. So, are you protecting your employees or placing them at even greater risk? I'll let you answer those questions but be honest!

Safety programs encompass a wide variety of work conditions that could result in a severe injury or fatality. Imagine the potential hazards that could result from poor implementation of:

- Lockout/Tagout
- Machine Guarding
- Forklift Operations
- Confined Spaces
- Conveyor Operations
- Respiratory Protection
- Personal Protective Equipment (PPE)
- Warehouse Operations
- Fall Protection
- Electrical Safety
- Sheet Metal Operations
- Power Press Operations
- Utilities
- Powerhouse Operations
- Environmental
- Clean Air
- Clean Water
- Storm Water Permits
- Tier I-II Reporting
- Hazardous Waste Operations
- Underground Storage Tanks
- Housekeeping, etc.

I've been involved in several associated hazards, from electrocutions, amputations, vehicle accidents, gas, or chemical releases and/or spills, slips and falls, environmental issues, and underground storage tanks. These hazards are real and dangerous to people and the environment.

Now, think about the risks to all your employees caused by having an unqualified or inexperienced safety manager. Here are some questions you may want to ask yourself: Is it worth the cost of your company? Is it worth the death of one or more of your employees? Is it worth your company's reputation? Is it worth the potential OSHA fines and legal costs? I believe it is not.

Every business can afford safety. The decision is whether they want to or not. Most safety consultants can and will suggest updates to your current safety programs (if you have them) or work with you to create programs, provide periodic inspections, and run fire and other emergency response drills.

Your insurance company should provide guidance and assistance at little to no cost. If your insurance company is not providing oversight, maybe you have the wrong insurance company protecting your business.

Each one of your employees deserves to be provided with a safe environment to work. If you're just now implementing your safety programs, get your employees engaged from the very beginning. First, it demonstrates your commitment to your employees. It shows that you want and respect their input. They're the ones performing the work. Who would know better as to the procedures necessary to protect themselves and their coworkers? Listening to their input provides them with ownership of the process, which in turn means that they will pay more attention to the details of the safety programs they have created.

If your employees were honest, they would tell you that they feel unsafe, that they worry about the possibility of being injured, maimed, or even killed. They know they're exposed to danger every day. For every action there is a reaction, and a costly one that could be devastating to your business and your employees' lives.

When was the last time you truly spoke to your employees about their safety? Is it a conversation that you avoid, knowing the potential consequences?

Safety is not a cost, it's an essential investment in your employees' lives. The future of your business depends on it, as do any positive influences you have created in your community.

The prevention of one accident, one incident, or one near miss could be the cost of saving your company. Just think about how many injuries your company has sustained in the last few months, as you read this book.

A safety plan starts with identifying all the potential hazards. Next, hire a competent safety professional accountable for implementing the correct procedures, which include action plans and personnel training.

Imagine the devastation that you could experience from a fire, chemical release, tornado, forklift accident, or amputation, and what it would cost to rebuild, pay for the medical costs, legal fees, OSHA fines, and to rebuild your reputation.

Safety is one thing you just cannot afford not to have.

CHAPTER 7

Expectations and Accountability

Caution costs you nothing. Lack of attention may cost you your life and your families future.

There are two words we're afraid to use today: **expectations** and **accountability**. As an owner, CEO, CFO, supervisor, HR Manager, and a member of the safety management structure, do you truly know how important it is to understand the meaning of each word?

Expectations 1: the act or state of expecting: anticipation in expectation of what would happen. 2a: something expected, e.g., not up to expectations for an economic recovery.

Accountability: the quality or state of being accountable, especially an obligation or willingness to accept responsibility or to account for one's actions, e.g., public officials lacking accountability.

So, now that you know the meaning of each word, do they have any impact on your position as a manager, supervisor, lead, CEO, or CFO? Do those members of executive staff, supervisors, and employees understand the expectations you have set for them? Have you unambiguously identified and explained your expectations for those under your supervision, or is it assumed that everyone knows?

If members of management, supervisors, and or employees have no idea of the safety expectations, how can they be held accountable? How many members of the executive staff, mid-level managers, supervisors, and employees have read the safety manual/policies? How many companies even have a manual that encompasses operations and identifies safety programs and policies?

To empower your mid-level managers, supervisors, and employees, they need to be involved in setting the expectations and held accountable for their involvement in creating safety programs, administering safety programs, training, discipline, mentoring, and adjusting programs as activities change.

Creating and implementing a safety committee will develop opportunities for employees, supervisors, and mid-level managers to be involved in many facets of the company's safety programs. Becoming a safety committee member can instill confidence in the safety activities and programs, demonstrate management's support to safety, and contribute to the expectations and accountability of everyone involved.

Discipline is a critical and vital part of sustaining an effective, productive, and successful safety campaign. Before we can hold someone accountable, we must provide them with the information we want them to follow, ensure that they understand that information, and train them to meet the specific expectations they are going to be held to.

Remember not every executive, mid-level manager, supervisor, or employee has the same expectations and accountability. Therefore, parameters need to be established and followed.

So, how do you manage your expectations and hold your employees accountable? Have you made the expectations clear? Does the employee fully understand what you're expecting and why? If your expectations regarding safety are not clear, it could contribute to an unsafe work environment. Being able to hold employees accountable for their actions is just as important as clear expectations. Are you using the evaluation process to ensure that the employees are being held accountable?

- Wear and maintain the appropriate and required PPE.

- Inspect the area, identify workplace hazards, and notify management of these potential hazards.
- Participate in the safety committee meetings.
- Suggest and or recommend a process to reduce potential hazards.
- Participate in safety training.
- Operate equipment with all required safety features in good working condition.
- Conduct daily powered industrial truck inspections.
- Be a part of the emergency response team.
- Promote good housekeeping within your work area.
- Assist other employees to reduce the potential for work-related injuries.

If you've provided clear expectations, your employees cannot say they were not informed. Now that the expectations are clear in the written sense, you should take the time to demonstrate to them how to complete the expectations, again, documenting that you have verbally and in writing provided, clear and concise, open discussion on what your expectations are.

Now that there is a complete understanding, it's time to hold your employees accountable for their actions. Visit worksites. Be observant and identify whether the employee or employees under your direction are meeting the expectations you have set forth. If not, take the time to discuss, document, and then follow up. The key is to be consistent.

As a seasoned safety professional, I'm asked how to manage millennials. Simply put, they are watching how you treat and manage the other employees. If you don't have control of the other employees, then you don't have control of the new, younger workers. Again, it's all about expectations and accountability.

They have the attitude, "If it does not work out here in my favor, I will walk down the street and find another position."

With production being the driving force, there is often very little time for the supervisors to do essential monitoring of their employees. At times, managers are expected to do more with less, while at the same time, they are expected to supervise a multitude of employees, which, in some cases, is unrealistic.

Expectations communicated well can create a sense of unity and ownership and keep employees focused on the objective and specific tasks at hand. Clear expectations also encourage employees to become more engaged in the process. Clear and concise expectations help in reducing stressful situations not only for the employees but for supervisors as well.

Expectations and performance goals go hand in hand and the employee's performance should be discussed on a routine basis. This will keep the employee on point and help avert future problems. This keeps the lines of communication open between employee and supervisor. This must be included in the HR performance standards to make this successful.

Expectations should be set for all executives, mid- and lower-level managers, and all employees. There should be no questions as to what is being asked and expected of everyone involved.

- Be specific in setting expectations.
- Create realistic expectations.
- Give positive acknowledgment for meeting or exceeding expectations.
- Provide consequences for not meeting expectations.

If you follow these simple suggestions, you will have a more harmonized workforce. As a manager, you must be sincere and genuine when acknowledging your employees for a job well done. Don't just say "great job" or "good job." What does that really mean? I had a manager who was notorious for that. Then one day during our training I said, "Explain to me what is a good job? What is a great job?" If you're going to tell me, I'm doing a good job and then tell ten others the same, what value does it really have?

Accountability can and should be done in both a positive and constructive manner. Employees need to know that there are consequences for their actions, otherwise, they will do what they want, when they want, and how they want without any fear of being held responsible.

Again, I've worked as a consultant with several companies that were afraid to actually hold employees and managers accountable. In some cases, they stopped doing drug testing because they knew they would lose 50 percent of their work force. When I heard these statements, I was livid. I can't believe that we allow staff to come to work possibly impaired either by alcohol or drugs. What about the employee working next to that person? Don't they need to be protected or is production more important than their safety?

What statement as a company your making? You can't tell me there isn't another person that could take over the position of a controller, operator, driver, laborer, forklift operator, welder, or any other position. I just can't believe that and won't ever accept that we cannot find or hire employees who will work without being under the influence. Injuries happen when employees come to work impaired.

Speaking of injuries, every employee and member of management should report all injuries and/or near misses without the fear of being punished for being the bearer of bad news. This could backfire and become an OSHA whistleblower complaint.

As a federal investigator for OSHA, I was responsible for conducting whistleblower complaints for employees voicing safety concerns and reporting injuries. Employees have the right to report and file injuries. If there is any retaliation from a simple writeup to changing shifts, lowering pay, changing jobs, or reducing hours this could be an issue.

I've had several employee complaints regarding not being properly trained to do a specific job. I would advise anyone who feels unsafe to perform a certain job function because they were not properly trained to do the following:

- Request training to do the work safely.
- Do another job that can be completed safely and for which you are properly trained.
- Call OSHA and explain your situation.

- One thing you must not do is leave the facility for any reason. If you do, and it can be proven, your claim will be denied.

How to File a Whistleblower Complaint

You have the right to file a whistleblower complaint with OSHA if you believe your employer retaliated against you for exercising your rights as an employee under the whistleblower protection laws enforced by OSHA. In states with OSHA-approved State Plans, employees may file complaints with Federal OSHA and with the State Plan. See the Whistleblower Protection Program website to learn more.

- **Online** - Use the Online Whistleblower Complaint Form
- **Fax/Mail/Email** - Complete the Online Whistleblower Complaint Form, or Send a Letter Describing Your Complaint
- **Fax, mail, or email** cithcr a letter describing your complaint or a printed copy of your completed Online Whistleblower Complaint Form to your local OSHA office. Please make sure that your correspondence includes your name, mailing address, email address, and telephone or fax number so we can contact you to follow up.
- **Telephone** - Call Your Local OSHA Office or 800-321-6742 (OSHA). Staff can discuss your complaint with you and respond to any questions you may have.
- **In Person** - Visit Your Local OSHA Office

OSHA staff can discuss your complaint with you and respond to any questions you may have.

During my career, I have consistently heard things like, "It's never going to happen if it hasn't yet," "It's not my job," "I don't have responsibility for that," and "I simply don't care because nothing is going to change."

What a commentary, especially when it involves everyone's safety.

When implementing safety plans/programs and training, you must have buy-in from employees. Safety is only as effective as the employees, upper management, and clear lines of communication between them. Employees must be engaged in the entire process and be active participants in safety inspections and committees.

The employees are the ones doing the significant amount of work. Who better to get information from to build successful and effective safety programs?

Supervisors should be held accountable for the safety and well-being of their employees. It's the responsibility of every supervisor to get their employees engaged in safety, to demonstrate the importance and value that every employee brings to the company, to listen, react, provide direction, train, and ask for feedback. As supervisors, we tend to think that employees should know what is expected without being told. This is not compatible with an effective safety program.

To have a well-running, efficient operation, your employees, supervisors and yes, even upper management, need to have clear, concise expectations provided to them. They should also be reinforced as the year moves forward. Normally, holding a quarterly meeting to go over expectations is quite reasonable, as this provides them with enough time to make the appropriate changes in their work, attitude, and ratings.

As I provide training to CEOs, COOs, CFOs, middle management, and first-line supervisors on this topic, I strongly encourage all participants to make sure that they do the following:

- Understand the expectations.
- Understand the time frames.
- Understand the process for follow-up.
  Understand the consequences   and yes, there are consequences, both positive and negative.
- Understand the purpose of accountability.
- Understand how to hold management, supervisors, and employees accountable.
- Understand the consequences of accountability.

Yes, these two words—expectations and accountability—can be very hard to accept and to manage. Why? Because we live in a society where people don't want to rock the boat, get others in trouble, or have our subordinates upset with our decisions to act based on their lack of performance.

Others don't want to take the time necessary to document actions or lack thereof, which creates an additional problem with tracking. You want to take the time to properly document people's activities so that during your discussions, you have exact information, including dates, times, issues and/or outcomes observed or identified.

Expectations: both the employer and the employee should have them and be upfront about them.

Employer expectations for workers include:

- Be on time.
- Dress appropriately.
- Understand and follow the safety policies.
- Wear the appropriate safety personal protective equipment (PPE).
- Don't operate equipment that you have not been trained on.
- Review and understand the Safety Data Sheets for your specific work areas.
- Know how to evacuate or shelter in place.
- Be trained prior to responding to medical emergencies.
- Know how to use a fire extinguisher and in what conditions.

Employee expectations for safety include:

- Specific training on the equipment to be operated.
- Specific PPE required for the specific job function.
- Training on the use of a fire extinguisher if applicable.
- Training on Safety Data Sheets for the chemicals and products in the specific work area assigned.
- Being medically cleared and properly fit for a respirator if required.

- Training on the site's Emergency Action Plans (EAP).
- A safe work environment free from all recognized safety hazards.
- Training on how to report a work-related injury.
- Training on how to report a fire, near miss, or unsafe act.

Most of these employee expectations for both the employer and employee are not only reasonable but also required by law.

Accountability is being responsible for one's work and accepting the repercussions of one's actions. Accountability goes both ways: the employer should hold the employee accountable for their actions, and the employee should hold the employer accountable for their actions.

The employer has several options for responding when an employee is not accountable for their actions, including discipline from verbal counseling; first, second, and third write-ups for the specific offense; and termination if the unsafe act warrants that type of discipline. Kinds of offenses warranting disciplinary action could include failure to lockout/tagout, circumventing a safety procedure, entering a confined space without permission or proper training, workplace violence, and operating a piece of equipment without being properly trained.

Without setting expectations for safety your employees cannot be held accountable so where does that leave you as a company.....exposed.

An employee who is instructed to work in an unsafe manner, e.g., without the appropriate training, tools, or PPE, and is then disciplined for reporting an injury or unsafe equipment should first communicate with their supervisor. Ideally, the supervisor's response will be to correct the hazard.

The employee has the right to contact OSHA and file a complaint and or a whistleblower complaint. The employee also has the right to refuse work until the specific safety hazard or violation has been remedied.

Just to recap: You as the CFO, CEO, COO, or supervisor should define expectations and make them clear and concise. Make sure every employee, supervisor, executive member, and employer knows precisely what is expected. Be clear on time frames, quality of the product, required documents, and information, then hold them accountable for their actions, noting where they exceed, meet, or fail to meet the expectations. Be fair, firm, honest, direct, and have documentation to substantiate your rating.

If you're not strong enough or you don't have the authority or the support of the executive staff or HR, rethink the process. Expectations without accountability have no specific value to anyone involved.

Again, if this is not driven by the CEO and truly supported by management, it's just another pointless paper chase.

If safety is the component of the expectations you're setting for your employees, then establish that employees are accountable for their safety and that they have complete ownership in this endeavor. By creating ownership for your employees, you're emphasizing how important safety is within your organization.

This process must be visible to everyone, demonstrating the importance of safety throughout. Create a process where all employees throughout the organization can have a voice. Allow the employees to develop, initiate, and follow up on how they want this to work. As the CEO, provide direction and support but only when you are called upon to do so. Empower the employees to figure out the difficult situations on their own until they need and ask for your assistance.

This shows that they own the program with the support of upper management. Employee empowerment is critical to success in creating expectations for safety.

Employees need to feel they have the right and the freedom to voice safety concerns, report injuries, or participate in OSHA activities without any fear of disciplinary action.

How do your employees feel? If you tell your employees that we want to achieve a "Zero Accident Rating" without the proper support for that goal, you're essentially telling them "Do Not Report Injuries." Is that honestly the message you want to send? Of course not. This should be avoided as it could end up costing you so much more in the long run.

Be consistent throughout your organization. Don't have one facility doing something completely different than the others. This creates confusion and dilutes the message of safety and employee empowerment as well as the expectation of safety for all employees, management, and executives.

Remember: Once expectations have been clearly identified, you as the CEO, CFO, or plant manager must ensure employees have the appropriate resources to have a safe and healthy environment. This includes staffing levels, PPE, machine guarding, preventative maintenance, training, funding, and time. Most critical is a commitment from the management; yes, even at the cost of production delays.

If you want to be a successful organization, then you must establish a system for success for your employees, management, and even your executive-level directors.

Acknowledge the efforts of your employees. A sincere gesture of appreciation can go a long way in motivating your staff to keep moving forward. Remember, the success of your business is because of the hard-working men and women of your company. When someone gets injured, make them feel that you care about them, that they're not just another number.

Company-wide expectations of accountability speak volumes about you as a leader, manager, supervisor, or CEO. By establishing individual, department, and company accountability, there is no room for anyone to feel or say, "It's not my responsibility" or "It's not my job." They are being held to a specific standard in which safety is everyone's job and responsibility.

Now that you have set the expectations and accountability for safety, what's next?

Compliance, enforcement, and disciplinary action. Well, not so fast hold on to that thought. You've worked hard to get to this point. Don't get me wrong, there are and should be consequences for actions that involve being unsafe, taking shortcuts, not wearing appropriate PPE, not getting permits signed, and failure to report injuries.

The consequences should match the infraction and should be fair, firm, and consistent.

If you don't hold your employees, supervisors, and managers accountable for their actions and the actions of those under them, then what example are you setting? The choice is yours: expectations and accountability or chaos.

The lives of your employees, supervisors, and management depend on it, and it will affect your business relationships, community involvement, and your bottom line!

CHAPTER 8

Safety: Is It a Critical Component of Your Organization?

Priorities come and go but the values of safety should be deeply rooted in your organization protecting your employees, families, and their communities.

"Sweetheart, be careful as you travel to the other facilities. The roads are slick, and we need you to come home safely. We can't make it without you."

Is safety a critical component of your organization? This is an important question for the success of every business, now more than ever before. Why is it so important? Name another department in your company that has such an effect on every aspect of your business, including finances, staffing, workers' compensation, medical costs, legal, and other aspects of your manufacturing, warehousing, utility, food processing, fabricating automotive, construction, and health-care industries.

Tell me what you consider the most critical components of your business and why? Write down five aspects of the department that makes it critical to the operations of your business. Then write down the individual's title who, manages this department, and how many employees report to him or her.

How many shifts do you have, and how many supervisors are on each shift? Tell me how important they are to the quality of your products being made. Then tell me what effect they have on the shipping, receiving, and/or transportation of your materials and/or products.

Now, think about what it costs to manufacture your product and the hours of pay it takes just to cover the cost of one work-related injury (5% x your incurred cost for injuries, one Serious/Other Than Serious OSHA violation (**$15,625**), one willful violation (**$156,259**), or a fatality? Then, think about the loss of time, legal fees, training, and direct and indirect costs. Is the picture getting clearer? Are those departments you deemed critical really that critical? Don't answer yet, take a few minutes to think about what I have just asked.

Tell me how many safety professionals are on your staff. How many shifts are in fact covered by a safety professional? Does your safety professional manage the administrative duties and the state and federal environmental aspects? Do they also manage your workers' compensation program, OSHA compliance, fire prevention, electrical safety, and training programs?

Safety is a 365-day, 24-hour component of every business if you care about your employees because they navigate hazardous work conditions. If safety is not a critical component of your business, your focus is not on the most important contributors to the success of your business, your employees.

As I stated in the previous chapters, safety costs. In some cases that cost cannot be assigned a monetary figure, as you cannot put a dollar value on a life.

Maybe at this point you should ponder the lives of your employees. Are they worth making safety the most critical component of your business? Yes, I know that production and quality are important; however, they wouldn't exist without the hard-working people who work for you. They deserve to be protected and valued every time they walk through the front door.

If safety is not a critical component of your business, then how valuable are your employees to the future success of your business?

We never talk about the why, and I don't understand that. When we examine the why and the true impact of safety for our employees, it goes deeper than we can imagine. It's not the widgets, it's not the number, it's not the quality, it's the employees. They create widgets. They ensure the quality of each product that is packaged, shipped, and used throughout the world.

So again, *why?*

As the CEO, CFO, or COO, you are responsible. You have the knowledge, you sign the documents, you review the reports, you sign the paychecks, and yet something is missing. Where is safety in the list of your priorities? Where does it fall in the company's core values? When was the last time you took the time to talk to your employees, encourage them, appreciate them, and value their lives, which include their families? Do you know if they have family members? Do you know if they have parents, they are taking care of? Are they foster parents to those in need? Are they Sunday school teachers, teaching God's values and purpose? Are they volunteers helping others in need? Are they single parents, doing all they can to make the lives of their children just a little bit better? Are they going to school to enhance their abilities?

Why should you get to know them? They are the signature of your company and every product they produce. They represent what your company stands for, the voice that speaks volumes in the community about how they are treated, managed, and respected.

Why should you get to know them? They affect everything your company stands for. They come to work because they love what they do, they come because others depend on them, they come because you allowed them an opportunity to do something special, they come to be a part of something bigger than they are.

So, let me ask you again: Is safety a critical component of your business? If the answer is "No," tell me why not.

Why should safety be a critical component of your organization? Because it makes sense. Safety enhances your bottom line, it creates business opportunities, it shows that you truly value your employees. Safety reduces the potential of OSHA fines, environmental issues, lost time, injuries, legal fees, and fatalities. This alone should move you to consider making safety the most critical component of your business.

Think for a moment about how much you've paid in the last five years in workers' compensation costs, insurance premiums, legal fees, and lost production, time, quality, and potential business.

Ask yourself again why safety isn't a critical component of your business. Only you can answer that.

CHAPTER 9

When Emergencies Happen, Who Do You Call?

This chapter is dedicated to the men and women who have risked their lives to save others. Nurses, doctors, first responders, police officers, and paramedics. Your courage, strength, and willingness to put others before yourself are not only courageous but a reflection of the true American spirit displayed in times of crisis.

Is it 911, your supervisor, and are you using a cellphone or landline, a decision that could have lasting implications during an emergency?

Are you prepared for an emergency? Have you identified the potential emergencies that could happen at your facility? Do you know how your employees will react to these potential hazards? Take a moment to think about these possibilities:

- Fires
- Floods, tornadoes, hurricanes, blizzards, and other inclement weather
- Rail incidents

- Active shooters
- Workplace violence
- Medical emergencies
- Bomb threats
- Forklift accidents
- Trucking incidents
- Explosions
- Gas and chemical releases
  When was the last time you truly ran a drill of any sort? Was there a critique? Do you have written emergency plans that include continuity of business operations? Do you have the required emergency equipment?
- Food
- Water
- Tape
- Flashlights
- Emergency generators
- Blankets
- Plastic
- Radios or other backup communication equipment
- Heavy equipment
- Medical equipment/supplies
- First aid and CPR training, including use of AEDs
- Designated gathering locations and an alternate command post
- Designated storage locations for all of the above

Emergencies happen when you least expect them. So, who are you going to call? The plant manager, HR manager, or head of security? Who is going to step up and provide the direction necessary when chaos strikes?

We talk about safety. We *say* it's number one, but in all actuality, is it? Do you have a safety professional? Do you support your safety professional with the resources and authority required? Do you hear your safety professionals when they say the company is not prepared for a minor incident, let alone a major catastrophe?

Think about it. How important is that safety professional now? Did you as the CEO go the route of hiring someone inexperienced to save a few dollars on the front end? Did you ask the hard and important questions during the interview process? Were you even involved in the interview process?

So, who are you going to call when disaster strikes? Remember: it's not *if* it will happen, it's *when*. When an emergency happens, you'll find out whether you're ready, whether you can handle it, and whether you have the resources.

These are questions that need to be asked every day. Don't be fooled by numbers, empty promises, lack of experience, lack of thorough inspection reports, and reassurances that everything is okay when we know that it is not okay, it hasn't been, and it won't be until we remove our blinders and start facing the truth.

Yes, the truth is hard to face, but so is the reality of someone being injured or killed. Can you handle that?

When injuries or accidents take place, is the call for a safety professional made? It's like the Ghostbusters: who are you going to call? In any emergency, accident, and even near miss, time is extremely crucial. This makes conducting frequent drills extremely important for everyone involved. Drills should be conducted on no less than a quarterly basis but obviously not on a regular schedule.

I've worked with several companies who came right out and stated during our OSHA 30 Hour Training they don't have fire drills on the other shifts, only day shift. Then they stated management doesn't allow the time necessary to actually run any of the drills. They were concerned about being he liable and accountable now that they know what's required by law.

How are your relationships with the LEPC (Local Emergency Planning Committee), local fire services, ambulance services, and travel bus services? How are you going to move your employees? Where are you going to move them if your main facility is going to be unusable for an extended time?

How much training in emergency preparedness has your management team been involved with? How many of your employees have been trained? Has anyone read the emergency plans? When was your last mass casualty drill?

Since 2019, we've been in an ongoing medical emergency with COVID-19 throughout the world. There is currently no known cure, although there are vaccines and treatments. Do you have a plan? What are you going to do to protect your employees? Are you staying informed with the information passed out by the CDC?

Did you know that there are recommendations for prevention and response?

- Avoid close contact with people who are sick.
- Avoid touching your eyes, nose, and mouth with unwashed hands.
- Wash your hands often with soap and water for at least twenty seconds or use an alcohol-based hand sanitizer that contains at least 60 percent alcohol if soap and water are not available.
- Stay home when you are sick.
- Cover your cough or sneeze with a tissue, then throw the tissue in the trash.
- Clean and disinfect frequently touched objects and surfaces.
- Wear a mask in close quarters or inside a building.
- Although the coronavirus continues to develop many variants, such as the omicron family, which cause more infections and spreads faster than the "original" SARS-CoV-2, we must continue to inform our employees and take the precautions as indicated by the CDC.
- How many of your employee's travel? Do they know what precautions to take? Have they been trained?
- Do you have employees that work in a health-care facility?

- Just think about the number of people we encounter every day, not knowing where they have been, what they have touched, the last time they washed their hands. Are they healthy? Have they been sick recently?
- I'm not saying we should run around in an extreme panic, but you must be aware of your surroundings and the people you encounter. Most of our business dealings are in crowded restaurants, bars, and other heavily patronized areas.

Are you actually prepared to effectively respond to an emergency and make the right call and provide the necessary information for an appropriate response (medical, fire, Haz-mat) ... Not if you haven't trained and trained again.

Facts from Fears

Be alert to others in the workplace who may be ill; however, do not panic! Your employees who are sick should stay home. Do you provide sick leave, or have you gone all in on "lean staffing?" Do you have a plan? Maybe offer work from home? In any case, keep your people informed.

So, when you make that cellphone call, are you aware that if you're on the boarder of another state or even city you must be very clear, making sure you indicate exactly what your location is. Why? Because towers pick up cell phone calls.

It's all about being informed and knowing how to protect your employees, maintain your business, and set an example for others to follow. It's always been said we're not even ready for seasonal influenza. Just look around at your facility and your operations, and ask the question, "Are we prepared?"

Do you have professionals that can manage an incident, explosion, fire, active shooter, natural disaster, overturned gasoline tanker, chemical release, or an amputation, an employee trapped in one of our machines, or under an overturned forklift?

Who is going to respond? Who has been trained? Do you have the necessary supplies, equipment, training, AEDs, blankets, food, tape, plastic, ice, and water just to name a few items? How seasoned is your safety professional, plant manager, public information officer?

Do you have an action plan? Or is your response going to go something like, "We didn't think it could happen here?" Well, think again.

So, who *are* you going to call when emergencies strike? The choice is yours; however, time is of the essence, and it could mean life or death depending on the situation. The choice of who you call is critical to your business, your employees, and the community. If your call isn't to the right person, the delay could have devastating effects on the survival of your business.

Some companies that I work with have a policy to where only the supervisor can make the call. The problem with that is time. Where is the supervisor, how long might it take to make the initial contact so the call can be made? Why not allow the employee to make the call? The quicker the fire department is called the quicker the response. Fire spreads rapidly. What begins as a small fire could become a fully engulfed force of nature destroying everything in sight.

It has been said that in an emergency, you should surround yourself with the people you trust. Those individuals will have your back, the life and sustainability of your business, and the lives of your employees. The call you make could cost your business hundreds of millions of dollars, lost investments, damaged equipment, lack of inventory, and future business. Most importantly, it could cost your employees and their families (and you cannot put a price tag on that).

Are you sure you have the right people in place? Take another look at your circle. Is there a change that needs to be made before chaos strikes? The next time you hold a management meeting with your executives and department heads, ask the hard questions: Are we ready for a disaster? Do we have a plan? Are the plans tested to ensure they work? Do we have the necessary resources and are they usefully placed? Are community resources available and ready? Have we practiced, critiqued, and practiced again to make sure everyone understands their roles and responsibilities, or are we relying on hoping and praying we'll never have to find out?

If you get the latter answer, it's time to make a significant change, otherwise, your business will perish, as it is not built on a solid foundation.

Keep in mind that it's not the size of the emergency that matters, it's who is going to manage the emergency and how. A simple trash-can fire can destroy an entire factory if not properly contained and extinguished. But how many employees know how to use a fire extinguisher? Do they know what kind of extinguisher to use on what type of fire? How many of those same employees are comfortable with trying to put out this fire? How many would say it's not my job and just turn and run the other way?

Just because you have the training in a controlled environment does not mean that when the disaster strikes, you'll respond. How many people are trained in CPR and the Heimlich maneuver? How many are actually going to respond?

In our world today, the phones are out, and everyone is taking videos instead of acting to help the person who needs it. It may be that no one wants to put themselves in a position where they can be questioned on their actions or lack thereof.

Yes, the call you make is important. The question that remains is whether the one you're calling is going to answer, especially during an emergency.

CHAPTER 10

Safety and the Bottom Line

There is no bottom line tomorrow if you're not safe today.

The cost of safety and the bottom line ... what does it mean? How does it affect employees, business, and future business? The fact is that safety enhances the bottom line. The better your investment, the more effective your safety programs are, and the more profitable your bottom line will be.

Safety costs, yes it does, but not having an effective safety program in place will cost even more. Isn't it a point that should be driven home?

The bottom line is affected by quality, production, and safety. It's sort of like the old fire triangle, where all four elements must be present for a fire to occur: fuel, heat, oxygen, and a chemical chain reaction now known as the "fire tetrahedron." In this case, the reaction is financial, not chemical, but you still won't get the reaction without all the components.

So, what place does safety have over production or quality? Look at it realistically. Safety affects every aspect of a business. It touches every department, every employee, and every business relationship. You decide how important safety is versus production and quality?

It's a question only you can answer. However, before you decide, please listen to my perspective and years of experience in safety, business, manufacturing, quality, and the bottom line. I understand the importance of the bottom line and that the reason you have a business is to make money and that the reason employees go to work is to make money to support their families and loved ones.

You're the CEO, CFO, COO, or president of your business, and the bottom line is to keep your doors open and have a significant profit at the end of the year. Your business plan identifies many contributing factors. It should include safety, the cost, the effect, and the employee. The safety of your employees has a more fundamental effect than any other aspect of your business.

How many operations of your business will be hindered? How many employee hours will you lose, both directly and indirectly? How many products will not get out on time? How many will pass QA that should not have? Imagine the cost of bringing in grief counselors for the number of employees on all shifts affected by a significant injury or death.

So, be honest. Can you tell me safety does not affect the bottom line? If you had or have an effective safety program, one supported by top management and supervisors and under which employees are held accountable for their involvement and actions regarding their safety and the safety of those working around them, I guarantee the positive effect on your bottom line would be significant.

How significant depends on how the safety program is managed, supported, and accepted. The key to increasing the bottom line is making safety a core value, not in words but in actions. You don't need to put up signs to acknowledge your commitment. It's more important to be seen. That's right, it costs no money to walk through the facility with your safety professional, but it does reflect your commitment to the safety program and to your employees.

I'm not suggesting you attend every safety committee meeting. What I am suggesting is that you require all minutes be sent to you for your review, comments, and support. Remember: by having knowledge of the safety issues and or concerns, you place yourself in an accountable position to ensure that any safety or environmental issues identified are being managed until they're abated. By having knowledge OSHA can cite you with a willful violation if the conditions were previously documented and you failed to address them.

You, as the CEO, CFO, COO, or president, are probably asking yourself why you would want to place yourself in that position. The answer is not as complex as you might think. It's being accountable for the safety of every person, no matter their position, title, or pay status.

The real profit of safety is when your employees are reunited with their loved ones when they return from work every day...It's a bottom line that is priceless, like a family's love.

Every CEO, CFO, and COO wants to have a positive influence on the bottom line. But what does that mean?

Take a moment to think about the answer to this question: How have your actions, or lack thereof, impacted the bottom line, positively or negatively? Write down five things you could change today to make a positive impact on the safety of your employees.

1.
2.
3.
4.
5.

Then write down five things you could do today to make an impact on your company's bottom line.

1.
2.
3.
4.
5.

Compare the two. Surprised? What's the common thread that increases the bottom line? Now, putting those words into action is totally up to you.

Let me ask you another question: Does the safety of your employees affect your workers' compensation costs? What about your legal costs? Overtime costs? Retraining costs? The impact on the community and their support? Future business? See, safety plays a more significant role in the bottom line than most executives want to admit. Why?

Many executives have very little knowledge when it comes to environmental and safety laws and standards. It's overwhelming to grasp the full extent that safety has on a business, from making safety data sheets (SDS) available to managing a disaster.

Today, what role and effect does your safety program have on your company's bottom line? How much is the lack of your investment in your safety program costing you every day? Is safety a critical component of your company?

The bottom line is, invest in your employees, and you will reap the benefits of efficiency, effectiveness, productivity, and increased quality. You owe it to your business, your investors, your clients, and those that have and will make your company thrive: your employees.

Safety *is* the bottom line. Without it, business as usual is nothing more than a game of Russian roulette. Ask yourself: Would you want somebody to play that game with you or one of your family members?

CHAPTER 11

What's a Life Worth?

Investing in the safety of an employee's life isn't expensive, it's priceless just ask their family members.

"Sweetheart, how would our kids ever make it without you? Please don't take chances with your life because it affects ours as well. I love you."

As we have discussed in previous chapters, how can you assign a price tag to the life of one of your employees? Companies frequently put their employees in situations where they are exposed to hazardous conditions, such as:

- Insufficient or improper training.
- Lack of knowledge of company policies and OSHA standards.
- Unguarded equipment.
- Exposed wiring.
- Lack of required PPE for the specific job they are performing.
- Trenching. (Consider the hazards associated with trenching. Trenching presents hazards that could include being buried alive or having the circulation to a multitude of body parts cut off. Is the coffin box positioned correctly? Are the employees aware of

the hazards? And is there emergency equipment available in case something does happen?) See Chapter 2.

These are just a few areas where employees are put into a no-win situation without any regard for their well-being.

Are you properly training your employees for the job or position you hired them for? Is it being presented in a language that they understand? Are you sure? Just because an employee nods their head does not mean they understand. I've been involved in many training seminars and have participated in audits that revealed that non-English-speaking employees were not adequately trained or did not understand the information.

Just imagine a worker doing a job in which they were trained but didn't fully understand the potential hazards due to a language barrier. The accident happens; the employee loses several fingers. How are you going to explain that? Proper training is one of the most important things an employee receives when coming onboard. The time taken to ensure the employee fully understands and is aware of the specific hazards speaks volumes about your training program but most importantly your company and the value you place on that employee. So, when planning training, remember that your training is the cornerstone of how the employee is going to succeed—or fail.

The lack of knowledge of OSHA standards and company policies also puts your employees in a hazardous environment. Do you train your employees on the OSHA standards? Do your employees know your policies, including who calls emergency services and when?

Depending on your type of business, the hazards listed above could play a significant role in the value you place on your employees. I've seen utility workers in trenches with no trench box and no means to get out safely from trenches that were ten feet deep and less than five feet wide. The trench box is often placed in the wrong position, and this could allow circulation to be cut off at the lower leg or foot. Due to the push to get work done quickly, the employees' health and well-being are jeopardized. Exposing your employees to a condition like this means the value you place on them is extremely low.

Can you really place a monetary figure on an employee's life? What if it was one of your family members?

Imagine that you allow untrained operators to drive company vehicles, forklifts, and aerial lifts without being trained. What messages are you sending to that employee, their immediate coworkers, and members of your management team?

First, these powered industrial vehicles are dangerous. To have an employee think about operating one of these without being properly trained and monitored could result in an accident, fatality, or OSHA citation.

Just a few months ago, I was conducting a 10-Hour OSHA training class and the discussion was very intense regarding confined spaces, especially permit-required confined spaces and how employees were entering without being trained, having the right equipment, or having the appropriate rescue team available. It's so hard for me to understand why employees take chances with their lives. Is it because their need for that paycheck drives them to make unsafe decisions? Is production and quality more important than safety?

I can't put a price tag on my life, so when employers put their employees at risk, I wonder if they feel that the employees are expendable and can simply be replaced? Wow, what a sad commentary on how certain employers value lives.

OSHA publishes a newsletter series called *OSHA Fatal Facts*. Read the articles, listed below.

"Asphyxiation in Sewer Line Manhole,"
Brief Description of Incident

> A construction foreman died from asphyxiation after entering a manhole with an uncontrolled hazardous atmosphere. Four construction workers were working in an inactive sewer system on a jobsite that was

unoccupied for over a week. A few minutes after they started working, the crew noticed that the foreman was missing, and a manhole cover was removed. While one worker called emergency services, a second worker entered the manhole to assist the foreman and found him unresponsive at the bottom of the $20^2/^3$ ft. manhole (see Figures 1 and 2). When the second worker became disoriented inside the manhole, another worker used a fan to blow fresh air into the manhole and the worker was able to climb out. The foreman was retrieved by fire department personnel and was later pronounced dead due to asphyxiation.

Incident Prevention

Employers must ensure each confined space in which workers may be assigned duties and each space that is a permit-required confined space (PRCS) is identified before starting work at a construction site (29 CFR 1926.1203(a)

Now that you've read the information regarding this incident, take a moment to think about the contributing factors: List a few of them.

1.

2.

3.

4.

"Engulfment in a Sugar Hopper,"
Brief Description of Incident

A temporary worker was fatally injured after falling through a sugar hopper and becoming engulfed by sugar. The fatality occurred in a marine cargo warehouse operation, where bulk granulated sugar from ships is transported to the warehouse for storage, bagging, and distribution. Sugar clumps often prevented the sugar from flowing freely through a hopper onto a conveyor belt during bagging. Two or three times per shift, workers would manually break up the clumps. This fatal incident occurred when the temporary worker was breaking up sugar clumps with a pole/ shovel while standing on a hardened sugar bridge at the top of the hopper (Figure 1). The sugar bridge collapsed. As the worker fell to the bottom of the hopper, his legs went through the chute where he was engulfed by sugar and suffocated.

Incident Prevention

After this incident, the host employer put into effect engineering and administrative controls for breaking up sugar clumps safely. The hopper was redesigned with a permanently affixed (welded) top screen. Workers were trained to break up sugar clumps by scraping the sugar across the screen using a material handling bucket while safely on the ground. A structure for attaching a horizontal lifeline was installed at the top of the hopper for the limited work activities requiring access. Safe work procedures for using the redesigned equipment were developed and incorporated into the workplace practices. To prevent similar incidents, temporary staffing agencies and host employers have a responsibility to properly train all employees and ensure that appropriate safety measures are present in workplaces before work begins.

Now that you've read the information regarding this incident take a moment to think about the contributing factors: List a few of them.

1.

2.

3.

4.

"*Warehouse Fall from Pallet Elevated by Forklift.*"
Brief Incident Description

A warehouse worker was fatally injured after falling seven feet from a wooden pallet elevated by a forklift.

The warehouse inventory was stored on steel storage racks with the highest shelves about eight feet above the concrete floor. It was common practice for warehouse workers to place one foot or both feet on a pallet and move inventory on the top shelf (see Figure 1) while a coworker lifted them to the top shelf using the forklift, even though the equipment was not designed for this purpose. At the time of the incident, the worker slipped on the pallet while moving inventory and fell. The worker was taken to the hospital where he died from his injuries a few days later.

Incident Prevention

Accessing warehouse storage shelves by lifting workers on pallets presents serious fall hazards. The employer must implement safe procedures and provide the proper equipment and training to prevent injuries and fatalities. Pallets are not designed for sitting or standing, nor should they be used for lifting workers with a forklift. Instead, employers should use manufacturer-approved personnel lifting platforms.

Now that you've read the information regarding this incident take a moment to think about the contributing factors: List a few of them.

1.

2.

3.

4.

Reality breaks your heart when you go to the OSHA website and see the number of fatalities and just how little value some companies put on their employees' lives. Look at the construction warning signs, "Kill/injure a worker: $7,500 and 5 years in jail. As of 2020, the fine for hitting a construction worker increased to $25,000. Similarly, drivers who disable traffic-control devices in a maintenance or highway construction zone will face fines between $100 and $1,000.

Further, according to the current figures from the Census of Fatal Occupational Injuries (CFOI), there were 4,764 fatal work injuries recorded in the United States in 2020, a 10.7 percent decrease from the 5,333 the previous year.

The bad news is that fatal falls were at the highest level in the twenty-six- year history of the CFOI. The data reflects the deaths of 1,008 construction workers in 2020. This is a staggering figure; it's 14.5 percent of the total fatal work injuries for that year.

Occupational falls accounted for an alarming 805 of the total number of workers killed in 2022. We should be asking ourselves why.

Most of the worker fatalities were preventable, so why are we continuing to see the same incidents repeated? Another great question. We need to place more value on our employees' lives. Maybe CEOs, plant managers, CFOs, and supervisors need to look at their employees as they would members of their own families. Would the risks be acceptable for their child or spouse doing that work? If more company leaders viewed the risks in this light, maybe then the death and injury numbers would drop.

Companies go all out to put signs and slogans up all over the facility to show that safety is #1. However, their actions say something entirely different. Is anyone paying attention to these signs and slogans in the first place? If safety were in fact #1, we would do a better job holding management, supervisors, and employees more accountable for their actions.

Ask any CEO or CFO what monetary value they place on their employees, and you will get a wide range of figures. OSHA can tell you what it will cost you monetarily for a willful or repeated violation: $156,259 as of January 2023. What they can't tell you, though, is the value of the life that was taken. In my opinion, if a worker dies on the job and management was aware of the circumstances, they should be held criminally liable.

While with OSHA, I actually saw a CEO come into the office and drop off a one-million-dollar check to settle his complaint.

When the CDC looks at the cost of a worker's life, it's a million-dollar figure. This includes hospital costs, workers' compensation, legal fees, and property loss. Is that an acceptable figure? What about the family? Was the employee the only source of income? How many family members' lives depended on the employee?

If companies truly value their employees, they would do more than just meet the minimum standard requirements set forth by OSHA to protect their employees. When I do trainings, it doesn't surprise me that companies fail to conduct fire drills: it infuriates the hell out of me. How can we be so complacent when the possibility of a fire, hazardous release, active shooter, or any other disaster, manmade or natural, is ever-present?

How many construction workers need to die before we slow down on our highways due to road work?

Have you ever heard of the "Dirty Dozen" list? And I'm not talking about Clint Eastwood.

It's compiled each year by the National Council for Occupational Safety and Health (COSH). They identify the most egregious companies that expose their employees to unsafe work environments and work practices.

However, companies on this list still have the financial means to continue their businesses. The sad part of that reality is that they continue to place their employees in unsafe and hazardous conditions.

The complete Dirty Dozen for 2022, in alphabetical order, are:

- Amazon, Alabama and nationwide: six dead at Bessemer warehouse; injury rates more than twice the industry average.
- Atlantic Coast Utilities/Laurence Moloney, Boston: two workers dead; company lies to get construction permits.
- Daikin America, Decatur, Alabama: three dead from toxic exposures

- Dollar General, nationwide: workers stabbed, shot, punched, and pistol-whipped; millions in OSHA fines for unsafe stores.
- Ernst Nursery & Farms, St. Paul, Oregon: farmworker dies during heat wave; company tells OSHA: "Employee [should] be accountable for how they push their body."
- Foundation Food Group/Gold Creek Foods, Gainesville, Georgia: six workers dead from nitrogen leak; company tries to block OSHA investigation, intimidates survivors.
- Hilton Hotels, nationwide: Service cuts create safety risks for workers and guests in a high-hazard industry.
- Kingspan Light + Air, Santa Ana, California: workers monitor indoor air at "green manufacturer," find high levels of pollution.
- Liox Cleaners/Wash Supply Laundromat, New York City: no COVID safety protocols, no ventilation, no protections from toxic chemicals; company shuts facility and fires workers.
- Mayfield Consumer Products, Mayfield, Kentucky: nine dead when company keeps workers on the job during tornado.
- Refresco, Wharton, New Jersey: bottling plant workers at risk from COVID-19, chemicals, and fires at firm, with repeat OSHA violations.
- Starbucks, nationwide: retail workers exposed to, infected with COVID-19; corporate giant fires workers organizing for better safety conditions.

Just imagine the lives that have been affected by the unscrupulous actions of these companies. Organizations that repeatedly violate OSHA standards need to be held accountable. These companies have something in common and that is putting the lives of their employees at risk, in some cases the ultimate sacrifice.

Jon Stinson, a senior safety consultant, and I were talking recently regarding the value of an employee's life. He stated that so-called accidents are attributed to unsafe behaviors of the employee in many of the accident investigations he has conducted.

I believe that it's twofold when you openly investigate the incidents. My experience has led me to conclude that due to the pressure of production and the bottom line, management has failed to enforce safety procedures, standards, and practices and failed to provide the necessary oversight to reduce and/or eliminate conditions that could result in a fatality.

Don't get me wrong: Employees at times do step outside of their role and do foolish acts to get things done in the name of the business. Employees make mistakes, create accidents, and jeopardize the safety and well-being of those around them. Should they be held accountable? The answer is a resounding "Yes."

There is no monetary figure that could ever replace the life of the employee who has died. No more hugs, no more I love yous, no chance to live happily ever after, no good-night kisses to the children that are left behind, and no more talks with the parents that should have gone beforehand. How can you put a value on memories, on plans to walk through life with a significant other?

CEOs, COOs, and CFOs say they value their employees. They know they're the most important asset the company has. So why do workers continue to lose their lives while companies just keep on doing the same thing and hoping that death won't knock on their door again?

How do you value the lives of your employees? Are their lives worth your business? Think about it for a moment. A parent of three little babies dies performing work that is critical to your operation. Yes, OSHA is going to fine you, and the family may even sue your company, but how do you value the loss of that employee? Do you try to forget about the other members of the family that depended on that employee?

It's safe to say that it's more than difficult, if not impossible, to value (calculate) the cost of a human life.

CHAPTER 12

The Lives Affected

Everyone is touched when an injury happens at work, the co-worker, the family, the community - no one is exempt.

Who are the people affected by the death of an employee? Do you know? Do you care? If one of your employees died today, how many lives would be destroyed? How many parents would be affected? How many wives and husbands would have to walk through life alone picking up the shattered pieces left behind in the name of business?

There are not too many jobs that are worth dying for. The military, law enforcement, nurses, firefighters: these jobs have an inherently dangerous aspect, and those performing these jobs and their families understand that danger, that possibility.

Even if there were only one life affected, that is one too many. We go to work every day expecting to return home and enjoy the ones we're with. Then tragedy strikes, a life is taken, and families are changed forever.

As the CEO, ask yourself what would happen if your loved one died at work today? How would your life be affected? How about the lives of your children? What about the parents that depend on you to help them? What about the first steps of your new baby, the birthdays, the graduations, the hugs, and kisses that will never be. Think about that before you put your employees into a dangerous situation.

Production, quality, shipping, and the overall emotional state of your company can and will be affected. How will you manage it? The lives affected specifically at work will find many expressions, such as anger, distancing, emotional highs and lows, and withdrawal. All of these will have a profound effect on your business.

We tend to forget about the families of those affected by workplace injuries and fatalities. It's my purpose in writing this book that we don't forget about those who are not seen. These are what I call the true faces of safety. These are the husbands and wives, babies and children, brothers and sisters, moms, and dads. These are the loved ones who cry out in the night with a voice you do not hear. They are deprived of emotional, physical, sexual, and spiritual support. They feel like they have no hope and no connection and feel desperate to keep the rest of their family together.

Remember the story of Lee Shelby; all the emotional pain suffered by those he loved and those in his immediate circle.

Do you realize the number of lives that are affected by one injury let alone a fatality?

How many CEOs, COOs, CFOs, and supervisors stay in touch with families that are in true suffering? Could you tell me their names? How many of you have even taken the time necessary to check on your employees? We talk about being a family, and about caring for one another. Are they just words, or are we practicing what we preach? Are we extending care and resources to family members in need? How about to their coworkers, who come to work every day still burdened by the event that has just taken place? Or, are you just doing the bare minimum?

Why is it important to be aware of your employees' emotional states? Because you can reduce the possibility of having another catastrophe. Your employees and their families' well-being can be the turning point in the success of your business.

Extend yourself, be involved, and touch the lives of those who have touched your life, your business, and the other employees called family.

CHAPTER 13

The Value of Safety

The value of safety is measured by commitment to your employees.

"God bless those who have died during the COVID-19 pandemic and let us all never forget the value of life."

Is there value in safety? Is there a commitment from the organization's CEO, CFO, and COO? When that commitment has been corroborated at the upper management level, is it being propagated to managers and supervisors and then employees?

If safety is, in fact, a core value of your company, it cannot be put off by other circumstances, no matter what they are. Safety is paramount and is rooted deeply as habit in every employee, supervisor, and member of management. During the president's speech (Donald Trump) on March 27, 2020, he indeed stated that safety is first at this time in our country, then life, then work, and the market. I was so taken aback by this due to the fact the message has been the economy first.

The success of a workplace safety program is reflected in a reduced number of injuries and incidents. However, don't let the numbers fool you. The engagement of employees involved in the safety programs reflects the commitment to the goals and objectives of the organization.

Remember, safety affects production, quality, sustainability, and future business.

What is the value of an employee's life...their family...the community?

I believe that we lost our values when we took God out of the schools, God out of our states, and God out of our prayers and families. Maybe, just maybe, if we let God back into our lives, our values will be so much more defined. I'm not perfect, and I'm not preaching; however, I am saying when God is in the center of all we say and do, our values are clear!

Value in safety is critical and plays a role in every department of your business. Safety should not be changed, altered, or modified because of convenience, production, or any other circumstance. That is the difference in making something a priority.

So, from this point on, values should be as follows:

- Employee safety
- Accountability
- Expectations
- Leadership
- Integrity
- Commitment
- Customer service
- Honesty
- Empowerment
- Ownership of your word

So, these ten (10) values should be the cornerstone of your business. No exceptions. These values speak to your employees, stockholders, business owners, clients, and future business partners and should never be diminished or devalued for any purpose.

Safety encompasses each of the above-listed core values. Let me ask you, how many of these values I just listed are a part of your company?

How many of them have been compromised in the name of production, quality, and just business?

Now ask yourself whether the compromise was worth it. How many unnecessary chances did you take in the name of the bottom line? How much has suffered by not making safety a core value? Your employees' lives, your company's name, your financial status, and your possible future business relationships?

Now, what changes to your company are you going to make regarding your core values?

Integrity, accountability, commitment, and respect should be the core values in every business. I was taught when I was younger by my dad, who told me these few things as I left for the military:

- Treat others as you want to be treated, no matter their position.
- Give back to others as you have been given to.
- Be humble and appreciate the work of those around you.
- Be accountable for your actions, as they have consequences.
- Be respectful, honest, and work hard until the job is done.

SSGT Harold Hatton, said, "Your work is your signature, and the job is not done until it is finished ... no matter how long it takes." I've held on to those values and work ethics they are never compromised for anyone or anything.

My company was founded on the following values:

- Integrity
- Respect
- Accountability
- Helping others be successful
- Doing the right thing all the time and before profits
- Passion and quality
- Diversity

My previous company, Safety By Design Consultant Services, may not have made a big financial splash, however, we were respected for the way we treated our clients, our influence in the Hispanic community, and the way I treated those who worked for us. I believe without those safety consultants who gave themselves to make a difference not only to our company but to our clients and communities, we could never have survived when the economy was struggling.

For me it wasn't about money, it was about doing the right thing: making safety affordable for every small business owner. The Hispanic workers who put themselves in the most dangerous positions just to feed their families deserved better. Our hearts were in the right place, we worked hard, and we cared about those in our communities and those who did the work.

Safety is a value that should never waver. Lives depend on it.

CHAPTER 14

The ROI of Safety

It's a Return on An Investment It's an Employees Life

ROI. What is it? Does it really have any meaning? It simply means Return on Investment. Industries that operate in a high-hazard environment or at significant risk of exposure have a vested interest in ROI. It has been estimated that every one dollar invested in injury prevention yields a return between two and six dollars. Now this may not excite a lot of people, but you must realize that is bottom-line profit. It's better to invest and reap the benefits than to pay an exorbitant amount of money out of the bottom line for things such as medical expenses, increased insurance premiums, and lost productivity, to name a few.

Understand that the investment you make today in your safety programs can far outweigh the cost of not investing. The total cost of work injuries in 2020 was $163.9 billion. This figure includes wage and productivity losses of $44.8 billion, medical expenses of $34.9 billion (about $110 per person in the US), and administrative expenses of $61.0 billion (about $190 per person in the US). This total also includes employers' uninsured costs of $12.8 billion (about $39 per person in the US), including the value of time lost by workers other than those with disabling injuries who are directly or indirectly involved in injuries, and the cost of time required to investigate injuries, write up injury reports, and so forth.

The total also includes damage to motor vehicles in work-related injuries of $4.3 billion (about $13 per person in the US) and fire losses of $6.2 billion (about $19 per person in the US). The cost per worker in 2020 was $1,100. This includes the value of goods or services each worker must produce to offset the cost of work injuries. It is *not* the average cost of a work-related injury. Cost per medically consulted injury in 2020 was $44,000, while the cost per death was $1,310,000. These figures include estimates of wage losses, medical expenses, administrative expenses, and employer costs but exclude property damage costs, except to motor vehicles.

The breakdown is as follows:

- $36.5 billion in administrative expenses
- $55.7 billion in medical costs
- $89.6 billion in wage and productivity losses
- $11.0 billion in employers' uninsured costs
- $3.2 billion in fire losses
- $2.2 billion in vehicle damages

To put that in terms everyone can understand, every worker in the United States must produce an additional $1,400 in goods and services each year to offset the cost of workplace injuries.

These costs can vary depending on the type of injuries. However, if we assume the average cost of an injury is $39,000 and the cost of death averages approximately $1.4 million, it is estimated that if a thousand companies nationwide invested an extra $5,000 each in safety management, according to the ROI, it would save them each $10,000–$30,000 in accident-related costs. On a more astounding note, it could save society $10,000,000–$30,000,000. That would be an investment worth making.

To have a positive return on your investment you need to have a culture that includes an effective safety management system.

Just like anything else in life, there are several myths regarding ROI on safety:

- Safety is too expensive
- PPE = Safety
- Training indicates a strong safety culture
- Inspections and audits will unveil all risks
- OSHA compliance is good enough
- Safety culture should be managed from the top down

As stated in the previous chapters, safety does have a price tag; the question is, are you willing to expose your company, your reputation, and, most of all, your employee's by thinking safety is too expensive? Safety is not a quick money-in-the-pocket proposition; therefore, it's viewed as an unnecessary expense. However, those who have not only invested in their companies but in their employees, have seen the fruits of their labor with a reduction in injuries and their associated costs and increases in morale and employee retention.

Safety affects production, quality, and profitability. These complement the other aspects of your business, therefore positively enhancing the bottom line. The investment in your employees' lives cannot be measured by what you get in return.

Personal protective equipment doesn't equal safety. PPE is the last resort in protecting your employees. Simply providing your employees with PPE without monitoring, engineering, adding administrative controls, and maintaining production equipment, you're providing is a false sense of security.

PPE is protective in essence but is not preventative. By issuing PPE, you didn't remove a hazard; you just placed a Band-Aid on a hazard that could be eliminated or reduced. Issuing PPE is more expensive, extensive, and creates more complexity in the process. PPE comes with completing an assessment, then proper selections of eye protection, hearing protection, foot protection, body protection, head protection, and hand protection for each specific work area or task.

Then comes care, maintenance, and storage. Supervisors must monitor to ensure that the employees are properly wearing the specified and required PPE.

So, do you think that PPE equals safety?

Safety training is not really an indicator of how strong of a safety culture your business has. Safety training is only as effective as the information received and acted on. Training is not necessarily a positive indicator that you have a sound and/or effective safety culture.

Training can become information overload and your employees retaining that information could be inconsistent. To fully ensure that your employees are receiving the information you're providing, you might consider knowledge-check questions at the end of your training. While you are conducting your walk-throughs, ask specific questions related to the training given to determine if they received the information provided.

The dilemma with inspections and audits is consistency. We all have our areas of expertise and how we evaluate certain operations or programs. If you're utilizing a checklist inspection that really narrows your focus on things that may be hazardous, but something's not a part of the inspection checklist, you may fail to observe or recognize the potential hazard.

I am a firm believer that the inspection process is only as effective as the person conducting the audit or inspection. If the person conducting the evaluation is not fully engaging the individuals and processes being evaluated, you have missed a great opportunity, not only for training but to establish an open dialog on what was observed and how it can be corrected. This aspect is important, because if the employee doesn't know or understand what you have identified as a deficiency, how are they expected to correct it? Furthermore, why wouldn't you address the issue and have it corrected immediately? We miss an opportunity to not only evaluate but educate.

I've been involved in many inspections where there was no educational component of the process. I inspected several manufacturing plants identifying machine guards that were not in place, specific PPE that wasn't being worn, forklift operators not conducting and documenting daily inspections. As a matter of fact, several safety issues were noted during the inspection, but the equipment was still being used.

After the second inspection, I got with the plant manager and safety specialist, and we discussed having a different approach. During this inspection, we would not only identify the safety issue, but we would also address it with the employee, understand and listen to their thought process. Then we could use this as a teaching method for everyone involved. We agreed that this created a more positive environment and employees were more receptive.

No matter how detailed the inspection, evaluation, or audit is, the thought that all safety issues can be identified is simply false. It is time consuming to conduct a thorough evaluation of an area, as each regulatory agency your organization is accountable to have its own list of requirements. There are many aspects within each of the governmental agencies listed below:

National Electric Code (NEC)
National Fire Protection Association (NFPA)
Occupational Safety and Health Administration (OSHA)
American National Standards Institute (ANSI)
Mine Safety and Health Administration (MSHA)
National Institute for Occupational Safety and Health (NIOSH)

It's not only the inspection process, but also the employees who are performing the work. A never-ending change of events makes it almost impossible to say that an inspection will identify all safety hazards and/or concerns. Employees continue to work and expose themselves to potential hazards by working carelessly, poor housekeeping, not wearing the appropriate PPE properly, and in some cases, operation of equipment they have not been trained on.

How thorough are you when doing an inspection? I went to a facility, and I began to look at the electronically controlled exit door. I asked if the power failed, would the doors fail open or shut. No one had the answer.

Inspections are a painstaking process and require everyone to be involved to identify, look, reason, and establish a means to correct any issues discovered.

Regarding OSHA, the first question I have is: Why would you as a company only want to meet the minimum requirements? The second question: Just because you meet their minimum requirements, does that mean your facility and employees are safe? Of course, not; many circumstances arise that put employees and companies in harm's way every second of every day.

OSHA has set forth minimum safety standards that are complex and not written to be completely understood by everyone, which makes this even more difficult. OSHA and their employees are the only ones who can actually interpret the standards, although many of us try.

Why would anyone think that just meeting minimal standards is acceptable? I always inform my clients, both present and past, to evaluate every situation and to always go beyond what is required, as it's all a matter of interpretation, and OSHA has the final word. If you exceed the standard, you don't have to look over your shoulder and worry about how you're going to be evaluated by the next OSHA inspector.

Imagine how your employees are going to feel when they understand that you're exceeding safety standards to protect their well-being.

When you start looking at doing just what is required, it could expose your employees and business to hazards that could be life-threatening or business-ending. It's like telling your employees to only put forth a 75 percent effort, and if we get in trouble or someone gets injured, we'll take that risk.

Just being compliant with crafting a safety manual and site-specific procedures does not mean you are in compliance with OSHA, NEC, NFPA, or any other standards or regulations or that your employees are free from workplace hazards. It simply says that your administrative systems are in order and that your required paperwork is in place. But safety is more than just written policies, procedures, and training.

Where does safety start and end? At the top. If you as the CEO want to build a strong safety culture, do most, if not all, of these items to make it happen:

- Lead by example
- Make safety a core value *NO Exceptions*
- Be an integral part of your safety program

You must establish expectations and then hold everyone accountable including yourself. Take a proactive step by making safety a value that cannot be diminished for any reason.

The simple question is: Are you ready to commit by investing in your employees and your business and build a foundation that will not only provide you with a positive ROI but a reputation that other companies will want to emulate?

No one said that safety was like a slot machine where you can just pull the handle and collect your winnings. ROI goes beyond the bottom line: we're talking about precious lives, and there is no price tag on those!

Safety is the value placed on an employee's life the ROI in investing in that employee is significant.

To fully understand the ROI on safety you must understand the direct and indirect costs. You may ask what that has to do with the ROI. For measuring data, safety costs can be divided into two categories: direct (hard) costs and indirect (soft) costs.

So, what is a direct cost? They are listed below:

- Safety staff salaries
- Accidents
- Incidents
- OSHA fines
- Penalties
- Insurance premiums (Worker's Compensation costs)
- Attorney's fees

Indirect costs are harder to account for, but some of those are listed below:

- Administrative costs
- Investigations
- Expenses to repair property damage
- Loss of production after an incident
- Morale
- Malingering
- Inability to attract skilled workers
- Additional training expenses
- Additional expenses for new hires
- Loss of reputation

Investing in your employees and ensuring that you have effective safety programs that will result in a profitable bot- tom line leaves an impact.

According to the OSHA, businesses see an average return of *$4 to $6 for every dollar invested* into their workplace safety programs.[i]

To get an idea of how ROI works, it's important to start by inspecting the actual cost of an injury. OSHA estimates that businesses in the US lose $2 billion each year because of worker injuries. Shockingly, this number reflects only direct costs. Chances are the indirect cost are much higher.

According to the CDC, indirect costs add up to $2.12 for every dollar lost in direct costs, bringing their estimate for the cost of a fatal workplace injury from $1.4 million to $3 million.

OSHA provides a formula to estimate indirect costs of an injury based on national averages:

Direct Cost x Cost Multiplier = Indirect Cost

[for examples go to osha.gov/safetypays/estimator]

This says nothing of the sales required to compensate for the costs over time. Look at the following example:

For a single burn injury, the direct costs average $37,389, and the indirect costs average $41,127 for a total cost of $78,516. It will require a company with a 3 percent profit margin of $1,370,930 in sales before the indirect costs alone are covered and $2,617,200 in sales to cover the total costs.

For example, the American Society of Safety Professionals reports that a fall-protection program implementation by a US construction company reduced their accident costs by 96 percent—from $4.25 to $0.18 per person-hour.

I use the example of Alcoa when I speak of ROI, as Mr. O'Neill decided to make safety more important than profits. This was unheard of. As of today, this is still the most powerful example of the benefits of placing safety as the most important value in your company. It wasn't only because Mr. O'Neill put the safety of his employees over profits, it was because he was committed to the process and cared enough about his employees to do something totally eccentric. He proved his point over the thirteen years he spent with Alcoa: he quintupled their earnings.

When he retired in 2000, employee safety was five times better than when he first took over. Despite the hard work, success, financial stability, and reinventing of the culture at Alcoa, health and safety managers across the country must continually prove themselves and their value to the executives, CFOs, and CEOs of companies.

His goal was to have zero injuries, a concept that changed the culture of how employees were to be protected. Today, companies tell me how many hours, days, and years they have gone without an injury, and after observing their work process, I wondered how they didn't have many severe injuries, or fatalities, let alone how they had zero.

The fact is that employees work hard, equipment fails, employees are rushed, and are asked to do more than time allows, and we still want to focus on zero injuries.

What we need to focus on is making sure we invest in safety and hold our employees, supervisors, and executive staff members accountable.

Understand that accidents happen. We need to look at the cause, if it's preventable, and make it so it doesn't happen again.

The ROI for safety is not simply what goes deep into your pockets, it goes beyond that. Show your employees that they're valued, and they are not interchangeable bodies.

I say, if you take care of your employees, treat them with respect, honor their hard work, and hear their voices, your company will have a tremendous ROI not only regarding safety but in regard to your business's reputation.

The sustainability and success of your business, and the life of every employee who makes your business function, are reasons to make an investment in their safety and well-being. We need to hold everyone accountable for every aspect of safety at home, work, and any social activities.

The reason to invest in safety is because the ROI is LIFE and that should be the bottom line.

[i] https://www.safetyservicescompany.com/blog/roi-of-safety/

CHAPTER 15

Life is Short. Why Gamble With It?

Employees must realize that their lives have value and work is just work.

This chapter is for employees to understand their value in life and at work. Life is short, but we continue to take so many chances that might end it. Why, I don't know. It seems like everyone is in such a hurry we forget to protect ourselves. From the time we get up and get ready for work, were exposing ourselves to many dangers, from getting into our car and not using our seat belts, to arriving at work and thinking you're invincible by not using the PPE that is required. As I stated before, if you're not being safe at home there is no way you're thinking about safety at work.

Life can be taken away in a matter of seconds, but we decide not to utilize the PPE necessary to protect us because it's in your locker or on your worktable and in the time it would take to walk back and get it, you could have had the job done. It's only going to take five minutes...really?

I was walking through a facility doing an inspection and I saw six people standing around as if they were holding a meeting. The difference was that they were standing under a large metal magnet that was dangling above their heads. I then yelled trying to get their attention, move to the side I was yelling in a loud voice move, move, move! Once I got down to the main level we got together and discuss the potential near miss. After our conversation the excuse was simply, we didn't look up, we were not aware of our surroundings. Yes, it could have been a tragic moment for everyone involved not to mention those left behind.

I have been involved with several manufacturing companies that have recently started a program that allows employees to put the reason(s) why they work down in writing or with a picture of their loved ones. In some cases, it's a pet, a wife, husband, child, or an entire family. The purpose is to make the employee think before they act, before they take that short cut, before they remove the guard, or fail to put on their PPE.

Another company had the family members write a letter to the mom, dad, brother, aunt, grandma, or grandpa describing how much they mean to them, how important they are in their lives. Some of the letters were so touching it brought tears to my eyes.

How many of us work like this every day. Were focused on the task at hand and never pay attention to the hazards around us.

How many times have you decided not to wear your PPE because the job was only going to take two, maybe five minutes? How many near misses have you been involved in that left you thankful you didn't get hurt? Once, twice? More than six? If your answer was one, that would still be one too many, wouldn't you agree?

I was at a manufacturing facility in Indiana. We were walking through conducting an initial review of the facility. Three of us have just retired from OSHA. What we observed was frightening. We had two contract employees in a permit required vessel doing work while the equipment was in operation.

There was no attendant, supervisor, ventilation system to force clean air, or air monitors, and the plant manager had no idea they were even on site. After getting their attention and asking them the process for entering a permit required confined space, the one employee stated, "Our boss said as long as we have our feet outside of the space, we technically were not in a permit required confined space." At this point, we were appalled and told them that they needed to depart the facility and get appropriate training before they hurt themselves. After speaking to the plant manager, we stated that could have easily been an OSHA fine in excess of $100,000.00. It makes you shake your head at the exposures employees put themselves into either by not knowing any better or by being directed by someone who has no knowledge of the OSHA standards.

It's like going through a whirlwind during initial orientation. You are given tons of paperwork to complete, safety videos to watch and your only thought is, "I can't wait for this to be over so I can get on the floor and do what I was hired to do." You want to get out on the floor to operate a piece of equipment that you have just a little knowledge on. Yet, you may have operated a piece of equipment at another facility, but you have no idea about this piece of equipment. How has it been maintained, when was it last inspected, do the light curtains work, are the guards in place? No real training or discussion about what is required, but they need to get production out and no time for anything else.

I was at a facility recently. When I went out on the production floor, I observed a woman operating a press. After observing a few minutes and looking at the equipment I noticed how she was sitting, how the area was cluttered, and several of the buttons to operate this equipment were black with no markings. I asked her how long she had been working and she stated it was her first day. I asked her how long was her training? She looked at me and said, "I was told just to press these two buttons and if anything happens, I was to get the supervisor." I couldn't believe that I heard. I just couldn't allow her to continue. I told her to shut the machine down, and that we would speak to her supervisor. Well, that went as well as could be expected.

Yes, I understand that she needed that job, she needed that paycheck, but not at the expense of her being injured.

Just think if I would have said nothing... her exposure was tremendous. Then it happens: you almost lose your fingers as the blade comes down. You take a deep breath, step back, look at your hand in amazement, and then your body begins to shake as you realize how lucky you just were. Your life is worth more, if not for you, for the ones you love.

Today is all about immediate gratification at any cost. We fail to think about how our actions affect those we're working for.

Take a minute, check your areas for hazards, ensure you have the right equipment to do your job and that it is in good working condition. The few minutes you take to properly prepare yourself could save your life.

We take life for granted, as if accidents are not going to happen to us. Then one day when we least expect it, we take that shortcut, we become complacent, and then tragedy strikes. The accident takes a finger, a hand, an eye, a scalp... maybe even a life. Although you may say this is pretty extreme, I can tell you it happens every day. Accidents take many lives way before their time. Studies show that most on-the-job accidents happen within the first year of employment. According to a 2022 analysis, Thursday is the most dangerous workday of the week when it comes to employees being killed. Monday is the day where most employees are injured.

Employees must value their own lives by never gambling on it in the name of business.

The construction industry is particularly challenging, with the possibility of many severe injuries just due to the nature of the work. It employs some of the most unskilled and untrained workers. These workers speak many different languages from Polish, to Croatian, and Spanish. How many of these employees get trained in their native language. How many of them truly understand they training they received. The working conditions alone create hazards, from slips, trips, and falls to unsafe machinery, the conditions of the ground, overhead power lines, heavy equipment operations, and pedestrian traffic.

We all come to work preoccupied with kids, significant others, home and car problems, financial and health concerns, and these consume our thoughts. We then take those conditions, to the work environment, and try to have a clear enough mind and thought process to operate safely in some extremely dangerous conditions.

Without thinking we gamble, we roll the dice, we play the game of Russian roulette. Sometimes we work in areas like trenches or confined spaces, or we work with high-voltage electricity, and we lose focus on our safety just for a brief moment. We didn't take the time necessary to secure the trench, monitor the atmosphere in the confined space, or wear the appropriate PPE to work around high-voltage electricity. What are we thinking?

Why do employers gamble with the safety and well-being of their employees? Why do employees allow themselves to risk everything in the name of business? Is it the job? Is it the paycheck? Is it worth the gamble? I would say not.

Chapter Takeaways

Chapter 1, Safety: An Investment or a Cost?

The faces of safety are many: the parents, significant others, husbands, wives, children, and babies who will grow up and never have an opportunity to say, "I love you" to their parent.

The cost of an injury or fatality can never be fully measured in dollars. How can you put a price on a life that means so much to someone else?

Chapter 2, The Price Tag

It's time employers invest not just in their companies, but in their employees. Investing in employee safety will create a severalfold return on every dollar.

Chapter 3, Seconds

Accidents can happen in the blink of an eye and change lives forever. Employees come to work with baggage every day: the work they're performing and what they need to do to protect themselves may not be at the forefront their minds. They're distracted, overwhelmed, and pressured to get the work out and then, tragedy strikes. Don't let three seconds destroy your employees' lives or your company's future.

Chapter 4, Reactive vs. Proactive

The cost of being reactive waiting until after an accident, injury, or death could cost millions of dollars. Why wait to take care of hazards until after an incident?

Chapter 5, Commitment to Safety

How committed are you to protecting your employees by providing the necessary resources, staffing, equipment, and training? How will you make sure you implement safety as a core component of your company's values?

Chapter 6, Safety: You Can't Afford Not to Have It

The lives of your employees and their families depend on your investment in safety. A well-thought-out, well-implemented safety program managed by a safety professional is a business function you can't afford not to include in your budget. You can't fake safety, you can't ignore it, and you can't half-ass it.

Chapter 7, Expectations and Accountability

Every employee, from the most junior to the C-suite, needs to know the company's safety expectations. Communicate these both formally and informally, verbally and in writing, and have the person being briefed acknowledge that they understand them. Encourage them to ask questions and recommend adjustments where they see a need. Make it known that *nobody* is exempt from safety procedures and back that up with disciplinary action if required. The choice is yours: expectations and accountability—or chaos.

Chapter 8, Is Safety a Critical Component of Your Organization?

It's time to evaluate your core values and ensure that safety is among them. A lack of commitment to safety can affect the orderly running of your company and its future. Customers and other companies may not want to do business with you if you have a stack of fines and violations or an extensive list of workplace injuries.

Chapter 9, When an Emergency Happens, Who Are You Going to Call?

Emergency planning: we talk about it but are we really trained, prepared, and ready to respond? Admittedly, we have many other tasks to manage. Training for emergencies takes time, effort, and resources most companies don't want to allocate. When chaos ensues, who are you going to call? The plant manager, the human resources manager, the utility foreman, or perhaps that safety professional that you decided not to hire?

Chapter 10, Safety and the Bottom Line

The bottom line: what does it really mean if you don't have a safety program? Safety isn't a cost but an investment that actually creates financial benefits. When we talk about the bottom line, we also must account for the value of your employees' lives and the effects on their families, your company, and the community.

Chapter 11, What's a Life Worth?

How can you assign a dollar value to your employees' lives? Every day you expose your employees to unsafe conditions within your workplace, that is exactly what you're doing. When you continue to put off equipment repairs and replacements, training, and safety infrastructure because you've been lucky so far and no one has been injured yet, you say a lot about the entire organization.

You can't put a price tag on an employee's life—it's priceless.

Chapter 12, The Lives Affected

As a CEO, CFO, or HR manager, how many times have you really thought about how an employee injury or death will affect their families? If this has happened at your organization, when was the last time you thought about reaching out? Who is going to comfort them? How do they move forward? Yes, they're going to get life insurance (you do provide life insurance for your employees, don't you?) and possibly some assets, but that can't bring back the person

THE FACES OF SAFETY - 115

who tucked them in at night, watched them score their first goal, watched them play their first solo, or walked them down the aisle.

Chapter 13, The Value of Safety

Safety must be a no-excuses, core component of every job, every department, and every product. A commitment to safety says that you value your employees. A lack of same says you see them as expendable. Value your employees and they will value you.

Chapter 14, The Cost of Safety

You can invest in safety, or you can bear the costs of not doing so. Every injury, every fine, and every lawsuit minimizes the potential increase in your bottom line. Safety affects how other companies view you as a potential asset or liability.

Chapter 15, ROI and Safety

Safety has a net positive ROI. It may not be seen daily in a monetary figure, but every employee who goes home safely after their shift represents money well invested. Treating your people with the same respect you expect brings an ROI that can't be measured in dollars. Don't gamble with the lives of your employees—invest in them.

Invest in a seasoned safety professional with a diverse background who stands by principles and demonstrates their integrity and sincerity with the way they communicate and treat every employee.

Chapter 16, Life Is Short—Don't Gamble with It

Life is precious, and it can be taken away at any moment. Why do we gamble with the lives who make our businesses successful? We push our employees to the brink for what?

As the CEO, CFO, or supervisor, how many times have you seen your employees in an unsafe position, for example areas where there are blocked exits, tripping hazards, fire hazards, chemical hazards, broken ladders, or pitted floors? How many times have you put them in an unsafe situation in the name of the bottom line? Do they operate a piece of equipment that is not properly functioning or is missing safety components? or example, guards, operative light curtains, foot pedals, and exposed electrical wiring, just to name a few? Are they insufficiently trained to run the equipment? Are they lacking PPE you should be providing (glasses, gloves, hearing protection, aprons, boots, hard hats)?

Ask yourself one simple question: Would I allow a family member to work in these conditions? If the answer is no, you must then ask yourself, why you're putting your employees in that position.

CHAPTER 22

Appendix

AED Automated External Defibrillator
CPR Cardiopulmonary Resuscitation
DOT Department of Transportation
EPA Environmental Protection Agency
MSDS Material Safety Data Sheet
NEC National Electric Code
NFPA National Fire Protection Agency
NIOSH National Institute of Occupational Safety and Health
OSHA Occupational Safety and Health Administration
PPE Personal Protective Equipment

References

[1] https://www.osha.gov/news/newsreleases/region5/02162023

[1] https://www.ehstoday.com/safety/article/21915925/nsc-2013-oneill-exemplifies-safety-leadership

[1] https://masslaywersweekly.com

[1] https://www.lion.com/lion-news/february-2021/can-i-go-to-jail-for-hazardous-waste-violations

[1] WorkClout https//www.workout.com

[1] https://www.ehstoday.com/safety-leadership/article/21238818/the-roi-of-safety-making-the-   business-case-for-safety-and-health

[1] https://www.safetyservicescompany.com

[1] https://www.optimumsafetymanagement.com/blog/roi-safety-management-system

[1] https://www.nsc.org/getmedia/d81515ce-57ba-4347-821e-4af731076260/journey-to-safety-excellence-safety-business-case-executives.pdf

[1] https://www.nsc.org/getmedia/9b0215b7-dc52-4b05-b1ae-42c875aaefb9/journey-to-safety-excellence-business-case-safety-practitioners.pdf

[1] https://www.isnetworld.com/en/

[1] https://www.avetta.com/expert-services

[1] https://www.merriam-webster.com/dictionary/expectation#examples

[1] https://www.merriam-webster.com/dictionary/accountability#examples

[1] https://www.osha.gov/sites/default/files/publications/OSHA3819.pdf

[1] https://www.osha.gov/sites/default/files/publications/OSHA3816.pdf

[1] https://glasgowolsson.com/cookcountycriminalattorneys/2020/02/28/penalties-hitting-construction-zone-worker-have-increased/

[1] https://www.bls.gov/news.release/cfoi.nr0.htm

[1] https://nationalcosh.org/2022-04_Announcing_The_Dirty_Dozen

[1] Dave Blanchard, *EHS Today*, May 29, 2018

[1] https://injuryfacts.nsc.org/work/costs/work-injury-costs/

[1] https://www.safetyservicescompany.com/blog/roi-of-safety/

[1] https://www.workhub.com/resources/blog/what-are-the-most-dangerous-days-for-workers

https://www.onsitesafety.com/safety-articles/the-day-of-the-week-with-most-accidents

David A. Ward Sr. is a dedicated, family-oriented person. He is married, with five adult children: Toby, David Jr., NaTasha, Candiss, and Kaylynn. He also has five grandchildren: Braedon, Brycen, Brennen, Gabriela, and Rio.

David spent six years in the United States Air Force, Security Police Squadron at RAF Lakenheath, England, and Offutt AFB Nebraska; twenty-three years with the Department of Justice Federal Bureau of Prisons (BOP) as a National Safety Examiner, Fire Chief, and EMT; and five years with the Occupational Safety and Health Administration (OSHA) as a Federal Investigator. He retired after thirty-four years of federal government service in May 2011.

After he retired from the government, he started his own safety consulting company, *Safety by Design Consulting Services* from 2011–17 and is currently a Senior Safety Consultant with Sentry Insurance/Parker Services.